"Let's forget all about business...."

He dismissed the whole reason for her visit. "I thought you were the sort of girl who wouldn't dare put her nose inside a man's house without a formal invitation."

Lisette stood up. "I apologize, Mr. Hamden. I didn't mean to intrude—"

He pulled her back beside him. "I'm not criticizing. I'm pleased you've come. And, Lisette—" his hand drew her face around "—the name's Rosco. Look, forget our quarrels and forget our traded insults. Forget everything except that we're together now."

"Forget...the girl who was here?"

"Wanda? You can put her out of your mind."

Yes, thought Lisette, *as easily as you'll put me out of your mind after you've made love to me and I've gone.*

LILIAN PEAKE
is also the author of these

Harlequin Presents

and these

Harlequin Romances

Many of these titles are available at your local bookseller.

For a free catalogue listing all available Harlequin Romances
and Harlequin Presents, send your name and address to:

HARLEQUIN READER SERVICE
1440 South Priest Drive, Tempe, AZ 85281
Canadian address: Stratford, Ontario N5A 6W2

LILIAN PEAKE

across a crowded room

Harlequin Books

TORONTO • LONDON • LOS ANGELES • AMSTERDAM
SYDNEY • HAMBURG • PARIS • STOCKHOLM • ATHENS • TOKYO

Harlequin Presents edition published December 1981
ISBN 0-373-10474-X

Original hardcover edition published in 1977
by Mills & Boon Limited

CHAPTER ONE

'IF I were on a desert island,' Lisette thought, clutching her glass, 'I couldn't be more alone.'

Yet the spacious room was crowded, the atmosphere overflowing with goodwill. Around the panelled walls, chairs stood as if patiently waiting to be occupied. They were modern in design and held a promise of comfort with elegance as befitted such a forward-looking and influential organisation as the town's Chamber of Trade and Industry, on whose premises the reception was being held.

But each chair would wait a long time for an occupant. At such a function most people preferred to stand, to mingle, to move from group to group. The organisation's aim, Lisette had been told by the secretary, who was a family friend, was to bring its members together to promote greater understanding of local needs and introduce them to businessmen and industrialists from outside the locality.

Lisette was new to the game. In the face of the professionalism which manifested itself around her, and in the almost exclusively male company in which she found herself, she was a raw recruit. She felt as unversed in the world of commerce and industry as a newborn baby in the art of living.

When a tray had come into her line of vision, which anyway had been blurred by a bad attack of nerves, Lisette had seized the first glass her hand could reach. If she had known that that glass had contained brandy, she would have replaced it on the tray. In her world brandy was used exclusively for medicinal purposes.

Since she was rarely ill, she had forgotten the effect its strength could have on her reflexes. She drank—and immediately choked. A table stood near and she lowered the glass on to it. In some distress, she searched for a handkerchief and mopped the tears which brimmed from her eyes. Pushing the handkerchief into her handbag, she did her best to recover her poise. Fearfully she glanced round, hoping that no one had noticed her body's embarrassing and slightly adolescent reaction to the potent liquid.

Someone had noticed. Across the crowded room stood a man, brown-haired, self-confident, with broad shoulders and a lean, athletic build. He was a head taller than any other man in that room. Not only was he taller, almost every one of his companions could have given him ten years and more.

He seemed completely at ease, as though he had attended many such receptions in the past. Judging by the amused glint in his eyes, and the mocking quirk of his mouth, all of which Lisette could discern even from that distance, he had witnessed her choking session from beginning to end.

She tried to tear her eyes from his, but they were caught fast, like a swimmer entangled in river weeds. She was drowning, too far gone even to strive for life-giving air, and he seemed in no hurry to give her back her ability to breathe. At last, having apparently looked his fill, the man turned away.

He had released her eyes and she breathed again. At once her sense of isolation returned and she wished she had not come. Odd, she reflected, how for a few moments she had not felt alone, although she had not moved a step, nor had anyone—least of all the stranger across the room—addressed a word to her.

If it had not been for her mother, she would have gone to the cloakroom, taken her coat and gone away.

If it had not been for her mother, she would not have been there at all.

'You're the head of our firm now,' her mother had said. 'Your father was a member of the Chamber of Trade for years, dear, and he always went to their annual receptions.'

'He was a man, Mother,' Lisette had replied, 'and the members are nearly all men. I wouldn't know what to say. I have nothing in common with any of them.'

'But you have,' her mother had insisted. 'You're in business just as they are. You have a factory to run. You're a business woman now, not a library assistant. You've got to think big, think business, not books.'

Think business, not books. How many times had she said to her mother, Let's sell the factory, invest the money we get for it, then I can go back to the library where I belong. I'm not made for this kind of life...

Her mother had shaken her head every time. 'I promised your dear father that after his death I'd keep the family business going,' she would say. 'We never had a son to pass it on to. I've only got you, dear, haven't I?'

Lisette had always winced at the implication that she had been a disappointment to her parents. Leslie, they would have called their son, after his father. She had never been allowed to forget that, as a girl, she had been second best.

If she had been a more practical, less feminine kind of person, she supposed she would have been challenged by the situation in which she found herself. To some women, it would have been a way of establishing their equality with the opposite sex, their equal ability to take charge, to wield power and get results.

Some women, she told herself agonisingly, would, even while proclaiming their equality, have wandered without embarrassment among these jovial-looking men. Quite unscrupulously they would have used their femininity to gain advantages over their masculine

9

counterparts. What man, these women would have argued, what businessman could resist giving orders for merchandise, in whatever shape or form, when coerced into parting with their firms' money by irresistible, womanly charms?

Lisette glanced down at herself. Womanly charms? Did she have any? A mirror told her she possessed near-black hair, a startlingly fair complexion, bright, intelligent hazel eyes and a piquant, well-shaped nose. It did not tell her—because she never smiled at her own reflection—that when laughing her wide mouth was inviting and that her whole face came alive.

It showed her a shape which would disappoint no normal male of the species. It would, in fact, attract and hold his attention. But these, she argued, were surface features. Womanly charm was more than the shape of a face or the possession of curves in the right places.

It was no good, she told herself, pulling gently at the tie belt of the clinging knitted dress she wore, she had to accept her personality as it was. It had been hers for twenty-five years now. There was nothing she—or her mother—could do to change it.

'Lisette, my dear child,' a short, grey-haired man startled her into the present, 'all alone? We can't have that.' He linked his arm in hers and she found herself walking with him. 'I have a guest who wants to meet you. He's intrigued, he says. A girl so young among a bunch of old men like us——'

'Mr Burlington,' Lisette said, trying without hurting the man's feelings to detach herself, 'I can't stay long. I must go very soon.'

She knew the guest to whom Mr Burlington referred. He was the man who had watched her from across the room and who had been so amused by her struggles to overcome the effects of the brandy she had inadvertently gulped down. Under no circumstances did she want to meet him. Anyone who could smile at her distress as he had done could only be obnoxious and overbearing and she had no desire whatever to make his acquaintance.

Stanley Burlington, owner of a handful of hi-fi stores, had no knowledge of the mental conflict taking place inside the girl who walked beside him. He saw her, not as a business woman, but as the young and pretty daughter of an old friend who had died. For his late friend's sake, if for no other reason, she must not be left out in the cold.

'Come, my dear,' he gave Lisette's arm a gentle tug, 'meet my guest, Rosco Hamden. Rosco, Lisette Baird, the late Leslie Baird's daughter.'

Lisette lifted her head and encountered the eyes which only a few minutes ago had ensnared hers. There was no disputing the mocking amusement now.

'Miss Baird.' A hand came out. With Mr Burlington smiling avuncularly at her side, Lisette had no choice but to put her hand in the outstretched one. The grip was firm. The hand was cold.

'Good evening, Mr Hamden.' Her voice was unnaturally high. To her annoyance, the words sounded prim and schoolgirlish. The smile that had pulled at his lips faded. So he was not impressed. Of course he wasn't! Hadn't she known she did not possess that precious commodity, womanly charm?

'A drink, Lisette,' Mr Burlington fussed, 'a drink.' A tray slid into view. He reached out and seized a glass. The man called Hamden took it from his host and replaced it on the tray, taking up another.

'Not brandy, I think, Stanley.' He handed the glass to Lisette. 'Sherry, Miss Baird? I think that might be more suited to your taste?' The smile was back but tinged with amusement.

Lisette coloured and shook her head. To refuse the drink and leave him holding it was her only means of

11

retaliation for his silent mockery. But she was deprived even of that.

'Come along, my dear,' Mr Burlington urged, 'you can't attend one of our receptions and refuse the food and drink.' He took the glass and urged it into her hand.

'So, Miss Baird,' Rosco Hamden said, 'you're a business woman?' The question was asked as if the questioner entertained doubts as to its validity.

Her eyes lifted boldly to his. She would not be thrown off balance by this man's provocation. 'Yes, Mr Hamden,' she replied, 'I run a factory in the town.'

Mr Burlington murmured to his guest, 'Family business, making shoes.' It was as if he had felt the need to make excuses for the firm. If he did, then she could not really blame him. It was not necessary to know the state of the firm's accounts in order to cast doubts on its effectiveness.

One look at the long, straggling line of huts which were its premises and which contained its production line—if that was what its manufacturing process could be called—was sufficient to make any astute business-man turn away in despair.

Mr Burlington's guest, however, could not know this. If she bluffed him into believing that the 'family business' which Mr Burlington had attempted to dismiss as of no consequence was instead a thriving, well organised concern, then she could hold up her head in front of this arrogant man.

For some curious reason, she experienced a strong desire to be well looked upon by him, to bring to those cool, appraising eyes—yes, they were grey, like a cloud-covered sky—a gleam of admiration for her managerial ability. His eyes did indeed gleam, but in an entirely masculine way, at the pink defiance in the face raised to his, at the gently curling black hair, at the arched brows and boldly innocent gaze.

Lisette did not feel a glow of feminine pleasure at his open approval of her attractions. What did it matter that this man, with his hard, handsome face, his calculating eyes, his attractive, attention-tugging appearance, thought her pleasant to look at? No doubt he gazed with that same eyebrow-lifting appreciation at all tolerably good-looking women in her own age group.

'I took the business over when my father died,' Lisette said in a voice strong with a confidence she did not feel. 'We design our own shoes. We cater for women and children.'

A voice from the crowd called, 'Hey there, Stan!' and Mr Burlington excused himself, saying he would be back. He was, he said, smiling benignly, leaving his old friend's daughter in good hands.

The possessor of those 'good hands' nodded to his host and turned to the girl beside him. 'Do you export your goods, Miss Baird?' His voice was impersonal and brisk.

Lisette congratulated herself on having succeeded in her aim to divert his attention from herself as a woman to her position in the world of business. Contrarily, she experienced also a twist of disappointment.

She nodded in answer to his question. 'We export to a number of countries, including Jamaica and the West Indies in general. But our greatest demand comes from home markets.' She did not add that those home markets were showing dismaying signs of slackening in their demand for Baird Shoes.

'Are your products of leather or——?'

She shook her head. 'Too expensive for the kind of market we cater for.'

'So you manufacture for the cheaper end?'

'Largely, yes. But,' she hastened to add, immediately on the defensive in the face of the hint of disapproval she thought she had detected, 'we supply multiple stores, chain stores and of course, the small shop-keepers.'

She searched his face for a reaction but found none. His expression was carefully blank.

'We have contacts in other countries, like—like Italy,' she went on, still intent on impressing this aloof stranger. 'The ideas for designs which they send us are sometimes impractical, but we alter them and adapt them for our requirements.'

He nodded as if understanding, but she saw she had only partly caught his interest.

'Am I boring you?' Lisette asked. She tried hard to sound sophisticatedly amused, but her tone of voice failed her miserably. Instead, the question sounded anxious and earnest.

The grey eyes flickered, then steadied to their original unreadability.

'On the contrary,' he answered with a slight smile, 'you intrigue me, Miss Baird. I'm struggling to picture you as a female tycoon, but failing lamentably. Tell me something. Is it successful, this family business you run, apparently so efficiently?'

The thump of a missed heartbeat, the faintest hesitation, then, straightening her shoulders, 'Of course.' But she could not lie without a quick rush of colour, so to cover it Lisette added, hoping to divert him yet again, 'Did you think that a woman taking over the running of a factory would inevitably give the company concerned the kiss of death?'

Again that faint smile. It was beginning to irritate her. 'Not necessarily. But an inexperienced woman,' a careless shrug, 'maybe.'

'So,' she simmered under his amused regard, 'you think I'm inexperienced?'

His cool eyes took on a different expression, dropped to the swelling shape under the stroke-soft angora wool of her dress, and lifted lazily to meet her infuriated

14

gaze. 'We're such strangers, Miss Baird,' he drawled, 'that I'm hardly in a position to know the answer to that question.'

Her eyes sparked. 'You're deliberately misunderstanding me, Mr Hamden.' She turned away.

A hand came to rest on her shoulder, detaining her and turning her back. 'At least we can part friends?' His other came out, extended towards her. As a business woman she could hardly disregard it. If it had not been accompanied by the faint smile, she would have placed her hand in his. But that smile and her better judgment was overtaken by a wish to get her own back —yet again—against this man.

She started to walk away.

'Lisette, forgive me, my dear,' Stanley Burlington, hurrying towards them, caught her arm. 'I was longer than I intended. I hope Rosco has been entertaining you?' He urged her back to face his guest. 'Not difficult to entertain, is she, Rosco? A pleasure to look at, eh?'

'A great pleasure,' was the mocking response. 'I couldn't keep my eyes off her.'

So with a few words, he had reduced her once more to the status of a mere woman. But hadn't she asked for it by reacting with such feminine pique to his gesture of friendliness?

Stanley Burlington's short, wiry body bent forward with laughter. It was plain that he had missed the sarcasm and heard only the masculine admiration implicit in the words.

'You know, Stanley,' his guest was speaking again, 'I'm astonished to hear that this young woman holds a managerial position in industry. Secretary? Yes, I could accept that. Bank clerk—that, too. Young wife with a baby crawling round the floor? That would fit the picture admirably. But executive, owner of a factory?' He shook his head, totally dismissing the idea.

'It's true, Rosco. When her father died——'

'She told me. It still doesn't make sense. Tell me, Miss Baird, this factory you run—does it produce the goods? Does it make a *profit*?'

Lisette bristled at his arrogance. The emphasis on the final word had been deliberate. It was meant as a challenge. If only she could rise to it and still remain truthful! 'Make a profit?' she echoed. There was the merest hesitation before she answered. She could not lie yet again without steeling herself to do so. 'Naturally it does.'

'Watch out, Lisette,' Stanley laughed. 'He's trying to trip you up. I can see that look in his eyes. He's on the scent of new prey.' His hand gripped Rosco Hamden's shoulder. 'This young man is an expert at scenting out a going concern, making an offer and,' he snapped his fingers, 'it's a takeover. Know who he is, my dear? When I introduced you to him I think I forgot to tell you. He's the chief executive, the head of Electro-Magnetic Universal, the electronics giant. You've heard of E.M.U.?'

'Emu products?' Lisette caught her breath and turned to the younger man. 'You're head of that firm —that organisation——?'

Rosco Hamden smiled. 'Conglomerate is the word I think you're looking for.'

It was, but she did not want him to know she could not think of it. 'Yes, of course, a——' How could she define it without giving herself away?

He explained, solving the problem. 'A corporation which, like ours, owns companies that are widely diversified. That is,' he smiled faintly, as if he knew he was telling her something of which she was not aware, 'companies that are not in the same line of business, like bakeries and car hire, television rental firms, insurance companies and hotel chains. You understand?'

'Of course,' she responded defiantly. 'I knew all the time.'

16

His eyebrows lifted but he did not comment.

'You're head of the firm?' she repeated. 'The—top man?' Did she have to sound so impressed, so sickeningly fawning?

He gave an ironic bow.

Stanley Burlington said with a smile, 'You see now, Lisette, who you're talking to. You see what I meant when I said he might be scenting prey where you're concerned.'

Startled, Lisette looked questioningly at Rosco Hamden, who said with a smile, 'So beware, Miss Baird, my company——'

'Conglomerate.'

His eyes glinted at her taunting correction.

'Company,' he persisted, 'eats little firms like yours for our mid-morning snack.'

'My firm is not for sale, Mr Hamden. Even if it were, I wouldn't let you buy it.'

A faint frown, a slight smile and he murmured, 'I'm intrigued. May I ask why?'

'I don't believe in monopolies,' she responded promptly. 'It's not right that giant companies like yours should keep swallowing up the "small man", that is, family firms like ours. I believe,' she finished, 'that big is bad and small is beautiful.'

Stanley Burlington gave a short, loud laugh. Rosco Hamden did not join him. He let his eyes wander over the stiffly defiant, entirely feminine figure in front of him, resting at last on the flushed, upturned face. 'On that,' he drawled, 'we are in complete agreement, Miss Baird.'

Her flush deepened. She was determined to keep the conversation impersonal. She would *force* him to keep his mind on business matters. 'Isn't it the current belief that an organisation can become too big and unwieldy, giving rise to labour and management troubles?'

'How many people do you employ?' Rosco Hamden asked curtly.

'About a hundred.'

'When you're head of a giant organisation employing thousands, Miss Baird, then—and only then—will you be qualified to discuss the pros and cons, the assets and drawbacks of large-scale management. Stanley,' he glanced at his watch, 'wasn't there someone you wanted me to meet? Goodbye, Miss Baird. I've enjoyed our discussion. We'll doubtless meet again. I shall be in the district for a few days.' With that he turned away.

Stanley pointed to a middle-aged woman seated and talking cheerfully to one or two others. 'There's Bette. Go and have a chat with her, Lisette. My wife will be delighted to have a word with you.'

Lisette nodded and watched as Mr Burlington led his guest to join a group which opened out to receive them. There were smiles, handshakes and general banter. There was no doubt about it, Lisette reflected, she was in a man's world. She would sink or swim according to her own efforts.

Baird Shoes *must* pull through. If it didn't, she would have to seek help—but on business terms. She would never, she told herself firmly, follow the example of many women and use her femininity where her bargaining powers might fail.

And never, she vowed, would she go running to a man like Rosco Hamden for a helping hand.

Lisette took a taxi home. She opened the front door and stood wearily in the hall, fighting a sense of failure. Before answering her mother's inevitable questions she had to compose herself.

There was no reason why she should feel so low and dispirited, and the sensation puzzled her. As she hung her coat in the cloakroom and glanced in the mirror, she saw that her cheeks were still flushed, her eyes still bright. They did not reflect her feelings.

The man called Rosco Hamden had remained all the evening at the reception, but he had not spoken to her again. Once, they had found themselves members of the same group. He had looked at her, but it had been while he was speaking to someone at his side and his mind had been not on her but the subject under discussion. It told her indisputably that her presence was less important to him than the glass of wine in his hand.

What was it like, Lisette wondered, to be as successful in the business world as Rosco Hamden? How were you treated when you were the chief executive of a concern as large as Electro-Magnetic Universal? As if you possessed god-like qualities? As if every word you spoke, every instruction you gave was the law?

She remembered how the chatter and noise around them had—to her, at any rate—seemed to fade into stillness as their eyes had met across that crowded room. And hadn't her heart played a trick, seeming to skid to a stop like a skier at the end of a run, then plod on heavily as the shock had passed? But if he had made an impact on her, she had certainly made none on him!

Her mother met her in the hall. A slightly-built woman of medium-height, she still did not look her age, widowed though she was. She tinted her hair, rigorously keeping the grey at bay. She cared deeply about clothes and as she greeted Lisette, she was as neatly dressed as if she, as well as her daughter, had attended the Chamber of Trade reception.

'How did it go, dear?' Her voice was excited, as if she were looking forward to an evening's gossiping about local traders who had been present, local personalities who had graced the event with their presence, not to mention any wives who might have accompanied their husbands.

Lisette's heart sank as she followed her mother into

the living-room. She had no inclination to talk. Instead she wanted to go up to her room, lie on the bed and think—about the factory, its finances, its troubled existence—and its future. That was something her mother did not know because she had deliberately kept from her how much the future of the factory was in doubt.

The living-room was long and narrow, but the height of its ceiling—in age the house was Victorian—and the fine quality of its decoration and furnishings lent it an appearance of spaciousness and luxury. The armchairs were wide and deep, their fabric a green brocade and only a year old, purchased when Leslie Baird had been alive and the family business in good shape—or so he had given them to believe.

Her mother occupied an armchair, sitting forward and clasping her hands. 'Tell me all about it,' Evelyn Baird said, watching her daughter sink on to the settee and push away her shoes. 'Did you meet any exciting people? Was there anyone who might be interested in our products?'

'Exciting people?' Lisette stared at the mock flames of the electric fire. She saw Rosco Hamden's face, his cool, calculating eyes, the eyes of a clever man, with a quick, competent brain. The eyes also of a connoisseur of womanly charms—those attributes in which she was so lacking. On second thoughts, she was not prepared to talk about the man. They would never meet again. But her mother waited so eagerly for an answer, Lisette sighed resignedly.

She should, she thought, be used to her mother's interrogations. They took place after every event which she attended on the firm's behalf. As co-director, she knew her mother was entitled to be told about the business contacts she made, about everything, in fact, connected with Baird Shoes, but it became harder every time to do as her mother desired.

'There were a lot of people there.' The words were meaningless, but her mother looked as intrigued as a child listening to the start of a fairy story. 'Mr Burlington, of course——'

Her mother nodded, adding, like a child who knew the list of characters off by heart, 'Of course. He's the secretary of the Chamber of Trade.'

'And——' Should she mention Mr Burlington's guest? She decided against it. 'And—and Carlo, you know, owner of Carlo's, the hairdressers.'

Evelyn lifted a hand and patted her hair, which was in perfect order. 'Which reminds me, I really must have it done. It's an absolute mess.'

One day, Lisette thought, she really would have to tell her mother to cut down on her visits to the hairdresser, not to mention patronising the most expensive dress shop in the town.

'And all the wives, of course,' she finished lamely.

'No one else? No one new?' her mother persisted, as if she had guessed that her daughter was withholding the best piece of gossip.

It was no use, she would have to tell her mother. 'There was a newcomer, a friend of Mr Burlington's.'

Evelyn's eyes lit up. 'In hi-fi, too, like Stanley?' She, as well as her late husband, knew the Burlingtons well.

Lisette laughed, she could not help it. Rosco Hamden, tall, arrogant, sardonic Rosco Hamden—*in hi-fi?*

She shook her head and braced herself for her mother's cry of joy. 'You know Emu products?' Her mother, eyes widening, nodded. 'Well, Mr Hamden's the head of Electro-Magnetic Universal.'

'No, really? The electronics firm? Oh, my dear, tell me, did he speak to you? What did he say? What is he like? My age, or——?'

Lisette managed a careless shrug. She had to persuade her mother, as well as herself, that the man was completely irrelevant to their way of life and that, despite his promise, so carelessly and conventionally given, they would not meet again.

'He's tall, athletic-looking, good features.' She closed her eyes and the man came to life. There was the proud lift of his head, the wide, dependable shoulders under the well-fitting jacket, the oval face narrowing to a rounded chin, the curving mouth with its quirk of cynical amusement. 'There's no doubting his intelligence.'

'Well, dear,' her mother remarked, 'for someone in his position, I suppose he has to have something that puts him above everyone else. Is he very old? I mean, nearing retirement?'

Lisette laughed out loud. 'I estimate that he was in his middle thirties.' She waited for her mother's astonishment to subside, then added, 'He also has a very high opinion of himself.'

Evelyn frowned. 'That's a little harsh, dear. After all, on such short acquaintance you can't really tell, can you?'

Lisette made a grudging movement conceding the point. Why did the man manage to rile her so? And, it had to be admitted, frighten her. *My company eats little firms like yours for our mid-morning snack.*

It was impossible to throw off the apprehension those taunting words of Rosco Hamden had aroused.

CHAPTER TWO

EVEN at her office desk, Lisette wore an overall. It was an uninspiring navy blue with collar, patch pockets and a tie belt. It did nothing for her. Not only did it hide her femininity, it levelled her personality to that of her working background.

The noise of the factory machinery penetrated even into her small, untidy office, where box files were scattered over shelves and files lay open on an ink-stained wooden table. Since money had become short, Lisette had had to dispense with the services of a secretary. She typed her own correspondence, answered the telephone and made her own calls and appointments. When the postman delivered the mail, she opened it herself.

It was early next morning and the letter opener had made a slit in the first envelope when there was the sound of a vehicle—car, van, lorry-load of supplies?—braking on the gravel outside. Lisette frowned. As far as she was aware, they expected no delivery that morning. Her diary certainly contained no appointments for that early hour. So who was the visitor?

There was a jangle of the hand bell which was stationed in a prominent place at the inquiry desk. It was really too dignified a name, Lisette considered, for the rough counter which was the first sight a visitor had of the interior. The inquiries desk was always empty, anyway, as there was no money to spare for that service, either.

Since Lisette was the nearest, it was always she who

answered the bell. Whether or not it was undignified for the part-owner of the establishment to do so, she never paused to consider. If she did not answer the summons, then no one would.

With a sigh of irritation she put down the half-opened letter and went into the corridor, turning right towards the entrance. Resting languidly, arms folded, against the counter was a tall, lean, brown-haired man. The moment he saw Lisette he smiled his irritating half-smile.

Why, at the sight of him, her heart should begin to race, Lisette was at a loss to understand. Not only was she confused by the sight of him, his presence there, his discovery of the exact style of the business which, the evening before, she had so proudly claimed to run, both appalled and dismayed her.

The newcomer eyed her up and down with a boldness made even more intolerable by the hint of amusement with which he carried out his survey. She realised the impression her careless appearance must be making on him and coloured under his regard. She wore no make-up, her overall was creased and in need of laundering, her shoes were low-heeled, black and fastened with laces.

In an illuminating and distressing flash of self-denigration she saw herself as he must be seeing her—so much a part of the disarray and disorganisation of her surroundings, she had taken on some of their slovenliness, too.

'What do you want?' Considering his position in life and his status in the business world, it was, she realised, hardly a fitting greeting, but she could not help herself. She was so shocked.

'I'm sorry to have taken you so much by surprise. If I'd known how busy you were, I would have telephoned your secretary for an appointment.'

He could have been speaking sincerely. On the other

hand, his words could have been pure sarcasm. Lisette's agitated brain was in no fit state to distinguish one from the other.

'I have no secretary.' The statement slipped out unguardedly and she watched the well-defined eyebrows lift.

He gestured to the inquiries desk. 'No girl at reception, either?'

'No.' His brows came together in a frown of disbelief. 'How——' She moistened her lips. She still had not recovered from seeing him standing there. 'How did you know where to find us?'

'Our mutual friend Stanley Burlington gave me directions. Why so surprised? I told you we would meet again, and I always keep my promises.'

'I'm sorry, I didn't believe you. There was no reason for us to meet again.' Her voice was low and toneless. 'I can't think why——'

'Don't tax your brain unnecessarily, Miss Baird,' he said with sarcasm. 'I'll give you the answer. Curiosity.' He looked around pointedly.

'Please come into my office.'

He straightened and followed, standing in the open doorway for a moment, as if it was necessary for him to adjust to the near-chaos. The faint smile broadened into a sardonic grin. 'The—er—executive suite, I presume?'

'I'm sorry I can't offer you the luxuries to which, in the course of your working life, you have no doubt become accustomed.' She swept a straight-backed chair free of trade newspapers and wished the legs of it were even so that the chair remained stable when occupied. To her relief, he refused, saying he would rather stand. He bent to pick up the discarded newspapers at the exact moment at which Lisette did so, and their heads bumped hard against each other.

It was Lisette who got the worst of it. Tears sprang

involuntarily to her eyes as she straightened and rubbed the painful area.

'I'm so sorry.' He took her wrist in cool fingers and gently stopped her hand in its rubbing motion. 'My head is obviously harder than yours. Not too much damage, I hope?'

She snatched her hand from his and turned away. Whatever happened, he must not see her tears. Anyway, she hated the touch of him. With a supreme effort she controlled her emotions, rubbed quickly and, she hoped, surreptitiously at the dampness and turned back. Rosco Hamden's face had undergone a change. The touch of something strangely like tenderness had gone and there was now an unexplained hardness in his eyes. The good humour seemed to have vanished, too.

He thrust his hands into his trouser pockets and wandered round, stepping over the files and folders and making his way to a shelf. Lisette had brought a selection of books from home and placed them haphazardly in a row. Some were still in their dust covers, others which were paperbacks were creased with use. She would read the books, sometimes for the second and third times, in her lunch hour, dipping into the sandwich box and eating the food her mother packed each morning.

'So,' came the sarcastic comment, 'the managing director of Baird Shoes is cultured enough to read. Real books, too, some of them tough going for a mere slip of a girl.' He half turned as if waiting for a reaction. He got it, and by his smile, it was the answer he wanted.

'Slip of a girl?' She rose spontaneously to his baiting. 'I'm twenty-five.' He turned back to read more book titles. 'Anyway,' she went on, fiddling with a ballpoint pen, 'I've never been able to bring myself to look on my job as one of a managing director.' He turned to face her, but she looked down at her desk. 'It's much too grand a name for my position. After all, you're a managing-director and look at the difference between us.'

As soon as she saw his smile and the lazy look in his eyes, she knew she had said the wrong thing. 'I certainly can see the difference,' he remarked, eyeing the softness of her hair, the wide, candid eyes, the inviting mouth, then lowering his gaze to dwell upon the rest of her. 'At least, I could last night. This morning in that —prison wardress's outfit, you look more'—he considered his words—'neuter than female.'

She frowned at his implied criticism, angry with him for his bluntness. For some reason, it hurt. 'I work for my living,' she retorted. '*I* don't sit with my feet up——'

'Meaning I do?' There was cold anger in his voice now.

She waited a moment, then said, 'I'm sorry, I had no intention of being rude.'

'I think you had every intention.'

'All right,' she said quickly, angry herself now, 'I did. But you were rude to *me*.'

'Not rude. Honest.'

She bit her lip and glanced at the pile of unopened post, then she looked at him. 'Did you——' How could she put it without being accused of rudeness again? 'Can I help you?'

He smiled. 'Ah, the old and tried—if tired—formula.' He looked over his shoulder through the door. The noise of the machinery was ceaseless. 'I just wondered if you would show me over the place.'

Now was her chance. 'Why, Mr Hamden,' she asked, wide-eyed, 'are you going to eat us for your mid-morning snack?'

Her twist of his words last night produced a cool smile. 'I'd find you very difficult to digest, Miss Baird. Before the digestion can work properly, the appetite has to be stimulated.' His eyes moved round the office and came to rest on her. 'I can see nothing within sight which stimulates my appetite at all.'

His meaning was painfully obvious. The insult was all the more painful for having been spoken with a smile, humourless though it was.

The telephone rang. Automatically Lisette's hand reached out. She listened and sighed. 'Yes, Mother, I'll pick the dress up on my way home. No, I won't forget.' As she replaced the receiver, Lisette said, 'Sorry about that. I have to answer all my own calls.'

He inclined his head.

'If you really want to see the factory, I'll show you round.'

'As I said, that's why I came.'

The noise of the machinery became louder as they approached the manfacturing area, the smell of adhesives, leather and man-made fabrics grew stronger. As she showed her visitor round, moving from bench to table, from cutter to machinist, from rows of half-finished multi-coloured uppers to soles awaiting heels and eventually to the pairs of completed shoes being placed side by side in white boxes, Lisette saw the drabness he must be seeing, the ancient, powered but hand-operated machinery, the primitive conditions in which the employees worked.

She felt like apologising. Instead, she walked proudly among the machinery and explained each process as well as her limited knowledge would allow. The workers helped, now and then putting in a correction or filling in when she paused, trying to think of the correct technical terms. She was sure the gaps in her knowledge were noted by her visitor, although he gave no outward sign.

When they returned at last to the comparative quiet of her office, a young man came from a room next door and stood in the entrance. 'Lisette,' he carried an armful of ledgers, 'could I have a word——?'

'Bob,' Lisette shook her head decisively, wishing she could give the young man some sign to be careful to give no secrets away, 'not now. Later. It will keep, won't it?' She finished intentionally on a note of appeal. 'You see, I have a visitor.'

The young man, tall, thin and wearing glasses, looked at the visitor, who looked back at him. They exchanged glances, the young man murmuring an amiable if slightly puzzled 'Good morning', the guest responding with a brief nod.

Bob, as Lisette had called him, appeared to have understood a little of the apprehension she had been trying to convey. He said, 'Fair enough. It'll keep. But not for long.'

Lisette's eyes darted across the desk to Rosco Hamden. How much had he gleaned from those four warning words? She could not tell, because his back was towards her. Once again he was studying her collection of books.

Bob left them.

'I'll make some coffee, Mr Hamden,' Lisette said brightly.

He turned from his contemplation of the books. 'You make that yourself, too?'

Lisette plugged in the kettle, found two pottery mugs. 'I do everything myself. I have to——' She stopped quickly and went on, trying to cover her slip, 'I prefer it. I——' she rushed on, seeing his air of puzzlement increasing, 'I look upon myself as a—a worker-director. It's more—well, democratic.'

She found a spoon and some sugar lumps in a box and handed him a mug of coffee. He refused the sugar and looked around at the chaos. 'I'd call it democracy run riot.' He leaned back against the shelving which reached to the ceiling, and sipped his steaming coffee. 'Precious near to anarchy, in fact.' That half-smile heralded the customary sarcasm. 'Have you really no control over inanimate objects?'

'Of *course*,' she snapped. 'I told you, I haven't got a secretary. If I had——' She stopped again. Now she was implying she would like one, but finances were short and . . . She tried again. 'I love order. I can't stand chaos.'

He looked around again, smiling sarcastically. 'It looks like it.'

She drank from her coffee mug, then put it on her desk. She swivelled her chair so that she faced him, crossing her legs, which immediately brought his keen eyes down to focus on the slimness of them. Lisette hardened herself to tolerate his lingering gaze.

'So,' he drank deeply, then held her eyes, 'you call yourself a worker-director. Why, I wonder? Were you elected by the people you employ to the position you hold? Or nominated by a trade union?'

She frowned, not understanding. 'As managing director? No, of course not. The business was my father's. When he died, I took it over. I'm sure I told you.'

'If,' Rosco Hamden persisted, 'you weren't elected by the employees, or nominated by a trade union, then I'm sorry to disillusion you, but you're not a worker-director. However much it might please you to look on yourself as one of them,' motioning with his head towards the main part of the factory, 'you're not. You're in a superior position, over them, their employer, the owner——'

'Part-owner, with my mother.'

He shrugged. 'It makes no difference. You're a fully fledged director,' he smiled ironically, 'by inheritance. Like myself, one of the privileged classes. There,' putting down his coffee mug beside hers, 'doesn't that hurt your equality-loving ego?'

It came to her with the shock of an explosion just what she was doing. She was entertaining to coffee the top man of an international organisation, a man with enormous power and influence, who was responsible for the handling of sums of money so large they were beyond her imagination, in what was little more than a dilapidated shed, in a room so cluttered with mess that she would be ashamed to bring even a casual passer-by into it.

Until that moment it had been, to her, merely a place in which to work. Now, as she glimpsed it momentarily through his critical and sophisticated eyes, it took on all the shoddiness of a slum dwelling. But did it really matter? Wouldn't it serve to jolt his smugness, show him at first hand something he might not have come across before—the facts of life of small businesses which did not possess the resources of giant companies?

All the same, the painful realisation of the contrast between her way of work and his forced her to say, in an unwilling attempt to apologise,

'I'm sorry——' How could she go on? Words would not sweep away the shabbiness. She stood, as if it was impolite of her to remain seated.

Rosco Hamden looked puzzled. 'Are you? For what?'

Didn't the man understand? Couldn't he guess what she was trying to say? 'For—for'—vaguely she gestured —'for all this. For not having a comfortable chair for you to sit on. For giving you coffee in a mug instead of bone china cups brought in by a—a——' She racked her brains. Who brought in the coffee in a large organisation? Her eyes sparked. She knew it would provoke, but who cared? 'By an underpaid, down-trodden tea lady.'

His eyes glinted, his jaw hardened.

'For,' Lisette went on, 'the irritating noise of the machinery, the unpleasant smells coming from the factory, the drabness, the ...' Her powers of description had let her down at last. Her voice tailed off to silence.

31

'No need to go on, Miss Baird,' he said curtly. 'I can sense failure in the atmosphere when it's there. And it is. I can smell defeat when it's all around me—as it is here—besides the odour of cowhide, adhesives, chemicals and other raw materials.'

'It's not true,' she cried, hating the lie but telling herself it was her only form of defence against this unbearably successful industrialist. 'We're a going concern.'

'Are you?' He came to stand in front of her, hands thrust in pockets, legs stiff and slightly apart. '*Are* you?'

She felt the impact of him as though he was touching her, physically maltreating her. She backed away but found her desk was just behind her. His eyes slitted, his lips tightened in a cynical smile.

'Were *you* the girl,' he said, 'who, only last evening, had the cheek to say to me, "Big is bad, small is beautiful"?' His eyes looked scathingly round the office. 'So small is *beautiful*, is it, Miss Baird? If you call this beautiful, you have a distorted idea of aesthetics, of the appreciation of beauty, not to say a twisted interpretation of good and bad.'

He was slating her, cutting her to little pieces. The edge to his voice made a deep incision in her sensitivity. She winced, unable to understand why a complete stranger, as this man was despite the fact that she had made his acquaintance the evening before, was able to hurt her so badly.

'It's as well,' Rosco Hamden said, 'that your business is *not* for sale, Miss Baird, because if it were, I should be the very last person on earth who would want to buy it.'

He went to the door. 'Thank you for showing me round. Thanks, also, for the coffee. That, if nothing else, has left a pleasant taste in my mouth.'

For a few moments Lisette stared at the emptiness Rosco Hamden had left behind. Only when Bob appeared in the doorway did she stir.

'Has he gone?' Bob asked. 'Good. Now we can get down to business.'

On her way home, Lisette collected the dress her mother had asked for. Evelyn Baird employed her own personal dressmaker for many of her clothes. A woman in her position, she argued, should never be seen wearing garments which could be recognised as coming from the racks of department stores.

Lisette was only too aware that her mother lived in the past, that she still looked on herself as the wife of the owner of a flourishing business and should therefore dress as well as her clothing allowance would permit.

There was no 'clothing allowance' nowadays, because she herself was part-owner of the business. Lisette often wondered whether she should restore that 'allowance', because she was certain that her mother spent far more on herself now that she had no husband to call a halt. Nor had she stopped buying luxuries—although she called them necessities—for the home.

The news which she had to pass on to her mother that evening would force upon them both a radical change in their way of life. What Lisette feared most was that her mother would not grasp the absolute necessity of spending less on everything, which included not only luxuries, but also some of the real necessities of life.

It was after their evening meal that Lisette introduced the subject. She braced herself for the spate of words which her mother would utter in an attempt to persuade herself that what her daughter was saying was not—could not be—true.

'Mother,' Lisette said, 'Bob Farrell came to see me today.'

Evelyn said brightly, as if pleased with herself that she could identify an employee of the firm, 'Oh, the young man from the accounts department.'

'He *is* the accounts department,' Lisette said patiently. Her mother nodded.

Lisette took a breath and jumped in at the deep end. 'We're in a mess, Mother. Bob and I discussed it this morning. The business is running at a loss. It has been for some time.'

For once, her mother was stunned to silence, then, with a bright, false smile, 'I can't believe it, dear. When your father was alive the factory was flourishing. Not,' she hastened to say with a flickering smile, 'that you're not doing your best, dear.' Her eyes took on a distant look. 'If only,' she murmured to herself, 'we'd had a son ...'

It was a wish that had often been uttered in Lisette's presence. She knew she should have grown used to it, but it had never ceased to hurt. She said, 'You're right, Mother, I am doing my best.'

Evelyn's eyes focused again and she saw the tautness of her daughter's lips.

'With very poor material,' Lisette finished.

'Whatever do you mean, dear?' Evelyn's voice sounded defenceless.

'Mother——' How could she explain? Lisette wondered. What she had to say would give her mother pain. 'We had a letter today from the shoe department of Carriers of London.'

'They're one of our best customers, aren't they?' Evelyn asked, looking at her daughter with a touch of smugness. Her eyes said, There, I remember something from when your father was alive!

'Were, Mother. Speak in the past tense. They're threatening to cancel the contract they made with us for a consignment of ladies' shoes.'

'But why?'

Lisette could hardly stand the bewilderment on her mother's face. 'Did Bernard get the design wrong?' her

34

mother went on. 'I thought he always showed their shoe buyer the design he had in mind and got his approval first before the shoe went into production?'

'Yes, he discussed the design with them. And they approved.' Lisette moved uncomfortably. 'It's not that. It's—well, to put it bluntly, we won't be able to deliver the goods on time.'

'But, Lisette, when your father was alive——'

'This never happened. I know, I know. But, Mother,' how could she get her message across? 'that was some time ago.'

She kept to herself the fact that even before her father died, things had been going badly wrong. But he had never confided in his wife. He had never ceased to shelter her from the realities of life.

Now she was part-owner, Lisette had decided it was time her mother was informed of the facts. All the same, she had to steel herself to do so.

She said, with as much patience as she could muster, 'I think I should put you in the picture, Mother.'

'Of course, dear. Like you, I am one of the directors.' Evelyn twitched her skirt decorously to cover her knees and settled back more comfortably in the depths of the armchair. It was, Lisette thought with wry amusement, as though she was preparing herself yet again to hear a fairy story.

Lisette said bluntly, 'The consignment of shoes won't be ready on time, for one very important reason. The machinery the workers are having to use to produce it on is so old it's constantly breaking down. Sometimes spare parts are needed and those spare parts either don't exist any more, or it takes weeks hunting them down. In other words, either we re-equip the factory with new machinery, or——' She stopped, unable to utter the ultimate blow.

'Or——?' Evelyn whispered.

'Or we close down.' There was a prolonged silence,

then, compassionately, commiseratingly, Lisette added, 'Those are the facts we have to face, Mother.'

'But—but your father ...' It was a weak attempt to ward off the truth. 'But, Lisette, why didn't *he*——' She could not go on, because she did not really know what it was she wanted to say.

'Why didn't he plough back some of the profits into the business and buy new machinery? Because——' Could she tell her mother another truth which would hurt her, maybe even more?

'He spent it all on you, Mother. And the house. The car, the expensive holidays you had abroad, the jewellery he bought you ...'

'Don't go on, dear. I know what you're trying to say. That I'm to blame.'

'Not really.' Even she was trying to shield her mother now, just as her father had done! 'It was—well, just circumstances.' For a long time they sat in silence, each immersed in their own thoughts.

Lisette said, her head back against a cushion, 'Rosco Hamden came to the factory today——' She broke off sharply, furious with herself for having mentioned the visit. Why had she done so? It must have been a subconscious wish on her part to find something, anything to alleviate the pain her mother must be feeling, something to take her mind off their troubles, even if only momentarily.

Her mother was alert at once. 'He did? Does it mean —oh, Lisette, does it mean he's interested——?'

'In the business?' Lisette shook her head decisively. 'You can forget that possibility entirely. He said——' She stopped herself again. Why did she not guard her tongue more closely?

'He said what, dear?'

Lisette affected a shrug. How could she say, He said that even if our business was for sale, he'd be the last person who would want to buy it? 'Oh, lots of things,'

36

she finished weakly. 'I showed him round and gave him coffee.'

Evelyn sat forward. 'What did he say, dear? He must have said something!'

'I think—I think he thought the place was a bit untidy,' Lisette improvised, complimenting herself on her question-dodging technique.

The telephone rang. 'Don't move, Mother, I'll go.' Lisette rose wearily. It was probably one of her friends. She felt in no mood for small talk. 'Bairds' residence,' she answered, then, changing her tone, 'yes, it's Lisette, Mr Burlington. You want my mother? She's coming. I'm—I'm fine, Mr Burlington. Er—yes, the factory's flourishing. Here's Mother.'

Evelyn took the receiver from her daughter. 'How *could* you tell him such an untruth, dear?' she reproached. 'Good evening, Stanley. Very well, thank you. And Bette? She's well? I'm pleased to hear it. Tomorrow evening? Why, Stanley, that would be lovely. Both of us? Yes, I'm sure Lisette's free.' She turned her back on her daughter's furiously shaking head. 'Lisette says yes, she is. I'd love a little chat, Stanley. I don't often go out now Leslie's not with me any more.' A few minutes later Evelyn put the phone down.

'Mother,' Lisette said, 'you might have asked me! I tried to tell you I didn't want to go.'

'Of course we must go, both of us. It occurred to me Stanley might help, give us his advice. After all, he is the secretary of the Chamber of Trade, and he's experienced in the business world. He must have come up against our sort of problem many times. I'm sure he'll have a solution——' A thought struck her, lighting up her eyes. 'Mr Hamden—he's staying with the Burlingtons—Stanley just said so. Chairman of E.M.U.! What better person to meet socially? With his money,' she clasped her hands, 'he might even be able to give us financial help, to tide us over——'

'Don't you dare, Mother,' Lisette cried, 'don't you *dare* mention the subject within a mile of that man! I won't go, Mother, unless you promise not to. I'll stay at home.'

Evelyn frowned, then smiled with cheerful resignation. 'All right, dear. I won't mention a word. Is that all right?'

Lisette sighed. 'It will have to be,' she said. But what she could not understand was how quickly her mother had been persuaded to agree.

The Burlingtons' living-room was furnished with reproduction antiques. It was a room in which Lisette never felt at ease. It lacked the warmth of deep armchairs which her own home possessed.

She had to admit, however, that the room was tasteful and cool in summer—but it wasn't always summer. Now it was early spring and the gas fire hissed from the fireplace from which the open fire had been removed and the opening boarded up.

Bette Burlington came in, her manicured hands extended in welcome, her tinted hair telling of regular visits to the hairdresser. She wore a neat brown wool dress which showed a simplicity of taste and which enhanced her slimness.

The settee was a small two-seater and it was this, when the initial greetings were over, that Stanley invited Lisette and her mother to occupy. As they fitted themselves into it side by side, Lisette found herself looking round as though something was missing. It was no use, she thought, trying to fool herself that she did not know for what she was seeking. The missing item was a man, tall and broad-shouldered, with a commanding presence and a self-assurance which stretched from the top of his brown head to the tips of his expensive shoes.

Moments later he came in, dominating the room with his air of authority. Lisette's heart leapt like a fish battling upwards against the current and spawning a myriad forbidden longings and desires.

His jacket was loose and casual, his polo-necked sweater emphasising the obstinacy of his jaw. The neatly-tailored line of his trousers hinted at the formidable strength of muscle in his long legs. His hair sprang abundantly as if it had recently been towelled after a shower. Thick eyebrows topped deep-set, intelligent eyes which, in no time at all, found what they were searching for and settled on that object with an enigmatic smile.

Lisette was glad her mother sat beside her. Under that sardonic scrutiny she wished she could persuade her mother to stay there beside her for the rest of the evening. With such a look in his eyes, Rosco Hamden seemed capable of anything—even breaking through the well-marked bounds of social politeness.

Introductions were made and after a mocking 'good evening' to her, Rosco concentrated on her mother. He took the chair beside Evelyn and talked to her as though he had known her for years.

Lisette experienced a feeling of relief, yet side by side with it came a sense of unaccountable irritation. If this was how he intended to treat her for the next two or three hours, then he could get lost! Something had made her dress with care, although her first instinct had been to pull on a skirt and sweater as an act of defiance against the man who, on leaving her factory the day before, had referred to it with such contempt.

Politeness had won, however, and she had decided for the sake of her host and hostess to bow to convention. The red dress with low-cut neckline and long sleeves suited her, and with its black patent leather belt drew attention to her slim waist. Her dark hair went its own way, parting off-centre and curling forward over her cheeks.

Stanley Burlington offered her a drink and asked awkward questions about the factory. If his distinguished guest had not been present, Lisette would have been much more honest about her difficulties. Although Rosco appeared to be giving all his attention to her mother, Lisette was certain that part of his mind was tuned in to her discussion with his host.

Stanley's wife, Bette, drew up a fireside chair and pushed her husband gently out of the way. 'Enough of your talking shop, Stan,' she said. 'Lisette and I are going to have a woman-to-woman chat.'

'Why,' said Stanley knowingly, 'has our young guest got problems? Man-trouble, maybe? That's what womanly chats are usually about.'

Lisette laughed disclaimingly. 'You're way off, Mr Burlington. Men don't *trouble* me.'

'Listen to her,' said Stanley, beaming, 'she's got so many boy-friends, has she, that she hasn't any need to lie awake at night like some girls who've got to twenty-five without a wedding ring on their finger, wondering whether any man's going to propose marriage? It's all that power she's got at the factory. It's gone to her head!'

'You don't know what you're talking about, love,' his wife reproved. 'She's got a young man, haven't you, Lisette? What's his name, Bob Farrell? You know, Stan, the brainy one who works with her at the factory. Good at figures.'

'Accounts——' Lisette began, but Stanley guffawed.

'Good at figures? I'll say he is, if he's Lisette's boy-friend!'

Lisette blushed and playfully hid her face.

'There, Stan, you've embarrassed her,' his wife reproached.

Stanley shook his head. 'She doesn't know her own charms, that girl.'

There was general laughter and Lisette realised that Rosco's conversation with her mother had ceased. His eyes were on her. They were narrow and evaluating and also strangely cold.

Bette stood, motioning with her hand. 'Come on, Rosco, change places. I want to talk to Evelyn. She's my generation, whereas this girl's yours.'

With seeming reluctance, Rosco obliged. As Lisette's eyes travelled the long distance up to his, her look was defiant, saying, If you don't want to sit beside me, I don't care! His eyes, following the same path over her as Stanley's had taken a few moments before, were hooded and unreadable.

He waited until his hostess had taken the seat beside Evelyn, then moved a pace or two. But he did not take the proffered place beside Lisette. Instead, he stood next to his host, who asked him if he would like another drink. Rosco nodded. As he waited, he returned to his study of the girl sitting alone on the settee.

'There's no need,' Lisette burst out, driven to anger, 'to sit beside me if you don't want to.' Why, she reproached herself, had she said those words? Now he would conclude that she *wanted* him to.

'I never do what I don't want to do, Miss Baird,' he responded coolly.

'Meaning that you always get your own way, Mr Hamden,' Lisette said sweetly, 'even if it means riding rough-shod over the wishes of others?'

He gave her smile for smile, but his eyes stayed cool. 'You have an imprecise mind, Miss Baird. I merely said I never do what I don't want to do. I didn't say I always got what I wanted. If you think about it, there's a difference.'

'What's all this "Miss Baird, Mr Hamden" nonsense?' Stanley demanded, returning with a drink for

41

Lisette as well as for Rosco. 'This is a social occasion. We're all friends together.' With a flourish of his hand, 'Let me introduce—Lisette, Rosco. Rosco, Lisette.' His wife called him. With a promise that he would return soon, he joined her as she talked to Evelyn.

'Do you know, Lisette,' Rosco said, having drunk from his glass, 'I think I'll take that seat beside you after all.'

A flash of pleasure shot through her as he spoke her name. It gave her a strange kind of courage to fence with him. She sipped from her glass, then said, 'Are you sure you *want* to, Mr Hamden?'

'Yes, *quite* sure.' His eyes, warm now, told her the reason—that she was female. This, to him, was clearly the sole attraction. 'And the name's Rosco.'

His unexpected curtness jolted her. 'I'm sorry, Rosco.'

He smiled, drank his glass empty and settled himself beside her. There seemed so much of him. All her senses came alive at his nearness. His shoulder and hip pressed against hers, his shaving lotion was subtle and exciting. The sight of his long legs which were stretched out beside hers aroused wayward desires. The sound of his voice was controlled and pleasing.

When he spoke again, however, she bristled, as he had surely intended her to do. 'Well,' he said, smiling down at her and removing her empty glass to a table, 'how's the dedicated worker-director this evening? Exhausted after a hard day trying to prove her equality with her employees?'

So he planned to irritate, did he? Well, she would not rise to him. Her eyes, wide and bright with a charm she did not know they possessed, turned upward to his. 'Very tired, Mr—er—Rosco. It's hard work trying to prove to the workers that you're as good as they are.'

His laughter rang out and when he looked at her again, there was a change in him. The cynicism had gone. Her unconscious gaiety had proved catching and his face had come alive. His good looks, his attractiveness caught at her feelings like brambles on to bare skin. If she pulled away, she knew she would get hurt. If she stayed impaled, the injury would be just as painful.

He said, with mock-seriousness, 'In the circumstances, you probably have an uphill struggle. You're both a woman and in charge, and any man, whatever his age, is suspicious of'—with a grin—'dare I say it?— a mere slip of a girl who has the audacity to think she's capable of taking charge.'

'I told you, didn't I,' she countered with annoyance, 'I'm not as young as you think. I'm——'

'Twenty-five. My junior by a good—or bad—ten years.'

'All the same, I'm fully mature——' By the look in his eyes, she knew it had been the wrong thing to say. Even her slight acquaintance with him should have told her to be more guarded when speaking to him. He was quick to seize every opportunity, it seemed, whether it concerned business—or pleasure.

'I think,' Stanley's voice broke into their conversation, 'we should consult our expert on this subject, Evelyn. Rosco,' Rosco Hamden's appreciative inspection of the girl sitting next to him seemed to end reluctantly, 'your advice is sought on a business matter by our good friend Evelyn here.'

Lisette caught her breath. What had her mother been saying? She had made a promise not to mention a word ... She clenched her hands on her lap, a fact which the man next to her did not fail to see.

Stanley said, 'A tricky situation, Rosco. Could you advise?'

Rosco Hamden pulled himself from his seat and pushed his hands into his trouser pockets. His good humour had submerged, lost to view, under a covering of thin ice. Lines furrowed his brow, he jingled coins impatiently and before speaking, took in the fact that the girl beside whom he had been sitting was as tense and nervous as a climber who senses the imminence of an avalanche.

He spoke, however, in a tone which suited the social nature of the occasion. With a smile, he said, 'I believe I'm now supposed to say, "I haven't got where I've got today without learning how to give advice on business matters." There, now I've said it. Go ahead, Stanley. I'm ready to receive.'

Was it only she, Lisette wondered, who could detect the irony, the veiled irritation in his words? It seemed so, judging by the pleased expression on the others' faces.

'Evelyn——' Stanley said, motioning with his hand, as if to say 'go ahead, he's listening'. But Evelyn shook her head.

'No, no, Stanley, you speak for us. You'll put it so much better than Lisette or myself.' She stole a quick, triumphant look at her daughter, who asked, her voice full of reproach,

'What are you doing, Mother?'

Evelyn shook her head, as if to say, 'Be quiet. Let the men talk.'

But Stanley, plainly uncomfortable, ran a finger round his collar. 'I don't really think it's for me to...' He tried again. 'It's my job, as secretary of the Chamber of Trade, to advise to the best of my ability, or to put our members in touch with those who might help. Beyond that——' He shrugged helplessly. 'You see, Evelyn, it's my belief that it's more than advice you need. It's——' He was too embarrassed to continue.

'What's the trouble, Mrs Baird?' Rosco's voice was abrupt, businesslike. Certainly it held no promise of help, Lisette decided agonisingly. How could her mother have discussed their problems in public like this? And after making a promise——

'Labour problems,' Rosco was saying, 'staff shortages, lack of orders?'

'Well,' Evelyn was taken aback at being addressed in such technical terms, 'I know I'm part-owner of the business, Rosco, but—well, it's my daughter who knows that side of it, really. Don't you, dear?'

Stanley, trying to ease the situation, laughed. 'She's passing the buck, Lisette. It's landed right there, in your lap.'

Lisette's eyes crept up to the grey ones a long way above. They gave no encouragement. 'Your move, Lisette,' the possessor of those eyes said evenly. So he was challenging her?

'Lisette?' She heard the appeal in her mother's voice. Here's your chance, her mother was urging. Take it with both hands.

All right, she would. Again her eyes sought Rosco's. 'As Mr Burlington says, Mr Hamden,' she stated boldly, 'it's not advice we need. It's money.'

There was a short, expectant silence. Stanley broke it. 'There now, Rosco, she couldn't have put it more bluntly if she'd been a child asking for a piece of chocolate!'

Lisette wished desperately that she could read Rosco Hamden's mind, but his face remained inscrutable.

Stanley persisted, his role as host clearly growing uncomfortable on his shoulders, 'What was it you said at the reception the other day, Rosco? That you eat little businesses like Lisette's for your——'

'Stanley,' the faint smile appeared, 'I—my company —confine our "eating" activities—our takeovers—to going concerns.' An abrupt change of tone, a sardonic glint accompanied the re-direction of his attention. 'Is *your* business a "going concern", Miss Baird? In other words, is it making money? Or is it losing it? The

45

answer's important. Think carefully before you answer.'

She looked up at him, her eyes flashing, defiant. 'You know very well——' Her teeth made indentations in her lip. No, he did not know everything. Could she bluff?

'I think, Stanley,' said Rosco Hamden, 'your young guest and I should have a talk. Let's mix business with pleasure, Miss Baird. Are you free tomorrow evening so that I can take you out to dinner?'

Go out to dinner with Rosco Hamden? The thought appalled her. 'I—I've got a date with Bob Farrell,' she lied. 'I'm sorry, I——'

'Rosco's only here for a couple more days, Lisette,' said Bette.

'You'll enjoy it,' Stanley encouraged. 'He's good company, even when he's talking shop.'

With a gleam in his eyes, Rosco said, 'How do you know what I talk about when I'm with a woman, Stanley?' A quick scan of the face of the girl who gazed up at him and he went on, 'I usually have—other things on my mind. Miss Baird, Lisette, allow me to present my credentials. I'm unmarried, unengaged, unencumbered——'

'Don't you believe it, Lisette,' Stanley said, 'he's trying to tell you there are no ladies in his life. Why, only the other day I saw you with——'

Rosco broke in swiftly, 'I said, "unencumbered", Stanley. There are a number of women in my life. One for every mood, in fact.' He asked, with a taunting smile, 'Well, will you dine with me, Lisette?'

'Big-headed, isn't he?' said Bette, nudging Evelyn, who laughed.

'I wasn't boasting, Bette,' Rosco responded. 'Just telling the truth.'

'Well,' Bette admitted, good-naturedly, 'you're handsome enough to have a queue of women waiting outside your door.'

'She's right, Rosco,' commented Stanley. 'Enjoy yourself before you settle down. And when you do, make sure it's the right girl.'

'Tell me, Stanley,' said Rosco, with a smile, 'you're a man of the world—how will I know?'

'Man of the world? *Me?* You've got the wrong person, Rosco. I'm just an innocent old married man.' They all laughed. 'But I'll tell you one thing. One look at the girl, and you'll know. Now, you two, make your date and we'll bring in the food.'

'Seven-thirty tomorrow evening, Lisette.' Rosco's voice was crisp. It was a statement. He had not asked a question.

Still Lisette tried to prevaricate. 'I told you,' she said, her tone annoyingly weak, 'I've already got a——'

'You can put Bob off, dear,' her mother interrupted urgently. 'He won't mind. He's a very understanding person, you know that.'

'Well?' Rosco persisted.

Lisette nodded resignedly. 'Seven-thirty. And—thanks.'

'What mood will *she* fit in with, Rosco?' Stanley teased.

'Ah,' Rosco's eyes contemplated his victim thoughtfully, 'now that depends.'

'On what, Rosco?' Bette asked with amused interest.

'On whom,' Rosco corrected. 'On Lisette. Who else?'

CHAPTER THREE

'PLEASE, darling,' Evelyn urged, 'be nice to him.'

'You mean do what I couldn't do if I'd been your son instead of your daughter?' The bitter words had come unbidden to Lisette's lips, but now they had been spoken, she could not edit them out, like cutting recording tape.

At her mother's shocked expression, Lisette added, thinking that a belated explanation might pacify, 'You've said so often, you and Father, how much you wished you'd had a son instead of a daughter.'

Now Evelyn looked penitent. 'Darling, I only meant —well, be pleasant to Mr Hamden and don't quarrel with him. He might—he just might be able to help us out of our troubles.'

Her mother's pleading tone, the way she reached up and kissed her daughter with moisture in her eyes, whispering, 'I don't know what I'd do without my daughter. A son would have left me long ago,' affected Lisette deeply.

Evelyn went on, 'You look so nice, dear.' She watched as Lisette picked up a coat, ready to put it on as soon as Rosco Hamden arrived to collect her.

The dress Lisette wore was white, the skirt falling in folds to the hem. Narrow shoulder straps supported the round-necked bodice which dipped low enough to tantalise the eye of any male escort. Over the dress, Lisette wore a matching long-sleeved loose jacket. Round her neck was a silver choker necklace and she wore matching silver earrings clipped to her ears.

Wherever he takes me, she thought, this outfit won't look out of place. She paced the room restlessly. Five minutes to go, five minutes before she would have to throw off this tension, this anxiety as to whether she had the ability to catch and hold the interest of the top man of Emu products for the duration of the evening.

It was a joke to tell herself that she, in her own way, held as privileged a place in business life as he did. Even when she was away from the premises, the ramshackle buildings which housed the factory of Baird Shoes weighed on her mind as heavily as they clung to her physical self when she was there. She could not throw off the feeling that she was a failure, along with the business.

Three prolonged rings had her pulling on her coat, waving to her mother and hurrying to the door. Rosco Hamden stood on the step as if expecting to be invited in. Lisette had no such intention. She wanted to avoid a meeting between her mother and her escort. After the broken promise of the evening before, she could not trust her mother not to start on the man as soon as he appeared before her.

Lisette could not deny the speeding up of her whole system at the sight of him. His eyes, keen and alert, his vitality, the magnetic quality which drew her so powerfully every time she was in his presence that she had physically to resist it—it was all there, encapsulated within that lean, relaxed figure on the doorstep.

She reminded herself forcibly of the reason for his invitation to spend the evening with him. There was nothing between them, no feeling, no attraction, not even friendship. Whatever the temptation to lower her guard and allow him to know that she enjoyed his company, she must resist it. She must even deny it to herself, however difficult it might prove.

The drive to the hotel did not take long. Soon they

49

were seated opposite each other at a table and he was looking her over uninhibitedly. In an effort to look sophisticated, she had fastened back her hair. She thought she had succeeded—until she saw him smile.

'So I'm entertaining your actual business woman, as they say. Efficient to her fingertips, a competent machine without emotion or feeling. A strict no-nonsense evening for me, I see.'

'Wasn't that the whole point?' she challenged. 'That this should be a business engagement?'

'M'm.' He picked up the menu. 'It's not impossible to mix business with—enjoyment. There are ways,' eyeing her over the top of the menu, 'of shall we say—coaxing a man into doing something which his better judgment—even his business judgment—tells him "no".'

'Are you—in a roundabout way, of course—inviting me to sleep with you, Mr Hamden?' Her voice was brittle, hiding the tight, sick feeling in her stomach.

'Miss Baird,' his eyes opened with mock astonishment, 'you shock me!'

She retorted at once, 'You wouldn't have said what you said to me just now to a man.'

He laughed out loud. 'You're damned right I wouldn't. I'm not that sort.'

'You would have taken a man seriously,' she persisted, angry with his light dismissal of her challenge, 'but because I'm female——'

'Your sex has nothing——' he stopped, his grey eyes dwelling momentarily on the rise and fall of her breasts, 'well, little to do with it.'

'You're admitting it,' she said bitterly. 'It's what my parents have said to each other, even in my presence, all my life. "If only we'd had a son."'

There was a brief silence and he glanced at her over the menu. 'Please forgive me.' Another pause, then, 'But if you're asking me to forget you're a woman, you're asking the impossible, I'm afraid.'

A waiter came to stand beside them and after suitable consultation, a choice of food and wine was made. When they were alone again Rosco said,

'It was your father, was it, who was the successful business man?'

Lisette answered carefully, wondering whether there was an underlying meaning, 'In what way?'

'In starting the family business and making it succeed. Or so Stanley Burlington told me.'

Of course, Mr Burlington would know only what her father had chosen to tell him, which would have been the successes and not the failures. She was not prepared to tell this man otherwise. In spite of the fact that she knew her mother hoped for a promise of help to emerge from this dinner engagement, Lisette did not want that help to come from Rosco Hamden. If necessary, she would play a charade of pretending that, despite appearances to the contrary, Baird Shoes would recover from its present troubles and start to thrive again.

Rosco said, 'You learnt the business, I assume, by acting as assistant to your father?' She did not reply immediately. 'Not Baird and Son,' he mused, 'but Baird and Daughter. An innovation, I imagine, but why not?'

Confused, she said, 'Did Mr Burlington tell you that?'

'Tell me what?' His smile did not fade.

'That I had been my father's assistant?'

'No, I just assumed you had been. How else could you be taught how to manage a business concern, how to produce profits at the end of each financial year and how to handle staff and so on?'

'Mr Hamden, I—I was trained as a librarian. That was what I was when my father died.'

The smile faded fast. The frown which took its place seemed to be fixed. She was sure it would crease his brow for ever.

'The name's Rosco, Lisette.' He said the words automatically, as if to give himself time to think.

Waiters approached, put plates in front of them, filled the plates and went away.

'A *librarian*?' he said at last. 'So you had no training for the job you're doing, no experience in factory management, no apprenticeship at all?'

'None whatsoever.' Lisette gave her first course little attention, her taste buds appreciating the flavour, her brain barely conscious that she was eating.

'Good God, no wonder the business is going downhill!'

So he was blaming her! She could have told him, 'But it was failing even before my father died. He spent any profits he made on my mother, holidays, drink...'

She could not, however, bring herself to be disloyal to a father she had loved, despite the fact that he, together with her mother, had by their attitude always managed to make her feel inadequate because she was a girl and not the boy they had longed for.

'I'm beginning to understand,' Rosco commented, drinking the wine which had been poured into the glasses on the table, 'why Baird Shoes is in trouble.'

'Because,' Lisette queried acidly, 'it's being run by a woman?'

'No. Because it's being run by a librarian.'

She felt her cheeks grow warm. 'I take exception to that, Mr Hamden. I also object to your implication that a librarian is unintelligent.'

'That's your interpretation of my remark, Miss Baird.' He matched her formality with his and it grated. 'How can a librarian have any knowledge of management techniques, the art of decision-making, the delegation of work, the establishment of good human relations?'

'I—I read about it—them. I took books from the shelves and studied them——'

'*Read* about it? Nothing else? You attended no courses on business management, for instance?'

'How could I? I had no time after my father died. Either I took over or the factory closed down.'

'Very commendable,' he said with heavy sarcasm. 'So you plunged in at the deep end although you were quite unable to swim?'

'It was a case of learning by bitter experience or drowning.' She gave a quick, challenging smile. 'I didn't drown.'

'Maybe not, but you're slowly but surely sinking. That you can't deny.'

'I do deny it, I do!' She felt like a child stamping her foot, except that her feet were crossed tautly at the ankles. 'All we need is a little time, a little money...' A lot of money, she thought, but did not say the words.

'Ah, now we have it. It's money you're after, is it?' She curled her toes, pressed her moist palms together. If he would offer his help, if he would say those magic words, 'How much do you need?', how would she react?

She didn't want his help, did she? She couldn't humble herself sufficiently to accept anything from this man. But, the thought crept into her mind like a child's hand seeking an adult's reassurance from a squeeze of the fingers, it wouldn't be for herself, would it? It would be for the business, for her mother, for the employees.

'I'm sorry, Miss Baird. Neither I nor my company are in business to act as money-lenders to failing firms.'

It was like a slap across the face.

'I'm not asking for money from you,' she retorted, endeavouring to keep her voice low, 'you're the last man I'd go to for *that*. I'm asking for nothing from you!'

Be nice to him, her mother had pleaded. Lisette felt the tears spring, looked down at her handbag, picked

53

it up from the floor and raked in it for a handkerchief. But even the dabbing of her eyes would give away her weakness to Rosco Hamden.

He had guessed already what it was she had been trying to hide. 'Experienced, sophisticated business women don't cry, Miss Baird,' he said softly. 'They grit their teeth, grow hard and brazen it out.'

Now he was mocking her and she was his inferior again. But, she thought bitterly, blowing her nose on the tissue she had found, how could she ever have imagined she was anything else?

'So you're asking for nothing from me?' said Rosco, indicating that she should pour the coffee which the waiter had placed on the table. 'I thought that was the main object of this meeting between us this evening? I thought Stanley said you were in need of help?'

As she poured, she thought, If I ask his advice, I'd have to tell him everything. Something inside her obstinately refused to allow her to reveal to the head of Electro-Magnetic Universal the very real difficulties Baird Shoes were in, the frail thread which could snap at any moment and on which the affairs of the business were suspended.

'Financial help, Mr Hamden,' she said doggedly. 'I've already told you.'

'Try your bank manger,' he said carelessly, almost as if he were washing his hands of the whole affair.

'We——' She stopped abruptly. She had so nearly said, We already have a very large bank overdraft which my father negotiated before he died. Now the bank is threatening to call it in ... 'We—might,' she finished, affecting a casual tone, as if the idea had not occurred to her.

'I could give you something else.'

She looked up quickly from her coffee which she stirred aimlessly. Suspicion clouded her eyes at the double meaning which seemed to thread through his words.

He smiled, as if he had guessed what was going through her mind. 'Not that. Not yet. Our acquaintance has been too short.' He watched the colour dye her cheeks. 'A girl like you needs—more time.'

'I'm sorry, Mr Hamden,' she said, wishing she did not grow so tense every time he became personal. 'We're on different wavelengths. You and I just don't seem to mix. I'm sorry also that you've had a wasted evening——' She pushed back her chair, but his hand came out and found hers, pulling her down again.

'I could teach you—quite a lot. And take that scowl off your face, Lisette. I'm not the lecher you seem to think I am.' She mumbled an apology. 'I could give you advice—on managerial matters, a kind of guide to a young librarian on how to become a business tycoon in three, or maybe four, easy lessons.'

She smiled in spite of herself, glancing at him shyly.

'That's better,' he said, his hand still on hers, 'that's much better.' He endeavoured to hold her eyes as well as her hand, but was unsuccessful. 'Well,' he persisted, 'do we establish a class in managerial studies with a ratio of one to one—one lecturer to one student?'

She tried to reclaim her hand, but he would not release it. With a shake of the head she replied, 'It's impossible, isn't it? In a day or two you'll be leaving——'

'I could come back, stay overnight at a hotel. My home is not all that far away. Less than an hour's journey by train or car from London. Or we could meet in London itself.'

'It's all so silly. Don't you see?' Her eyes willed him to understand. 'And anyway, what good would it do?'

'It might help to save your company. Who knows,' he smiled, 'after tuition from me, you might even get ideas of expanding!'

It was difficult not to smile. If only he knew how she

and Bob were struggling to prevent any further contraction of the business, let alone entertaining ideas of growing larger!

'May I—well, think about it?' Had that satisfied him, stopped him pressing for an immediate answer?

'Certainly. After all, a busy executive like you would have to consult her diary, wouldn't she, before committing herself to any appointments?'

Lisette heard the mockery but did her best to shrug it off. She wondered if he would take her straight home now the meal was over, but as they left the dining-room he motioned her towards an area through double glass doors over which were the words 'Residents' Lounge'.

'But,' she held back, 'we're not residents.'

He cupped her elbow, gripping it. 'Do you honestly think anyone will question us?'

No, she thought, feeling herself propelled through the doors and towards a settee, of course not. With this man's self-confidence, not to mention his intimidating height, no one would dare to challenge him.

Lisette sat herself in a corner of the settee, glad that it was large enough for four. He, she was certain, would take up his position in the other corner, which would mean there would be two cushions' width between them.

He did no such thing. He lowered himself beside her, so close it was as though there were not just two, but three other people occupying the settee instead of only themselves. He seemed, she decided sourly, to like the feel of women against him.

She recalled how he had sat as close as this at the Burlingtons' house. There, he might have had an excuse because the settee was so small. This one, being in a public room, was twice the size, yet here he was with his arm against her arm, his thigh against hers.

He was, she decided, a very sensual man. He disturbed her inordinately. With apprehension she felt the familiar quickening of her pulse rate, the stirring into life of all her senses. To her dismay, it seemed to happen every time he came near, each time, in fact, that she saw him.

Shying away from any but the lightest physical contact with the opposite sex, she tightened her muscles to such an extent that she managed to draw back from the touch of his shoulder and arm. Then she crossed her legs in a slow, delicate action, cutting off contact there, too.

She felt his eyes on her, but she pretended indifference. 'What's the matter,' he asked abruptly, 'wouldn't your boy-friend approve of our nearness? What's his name—Farrell? I thought—in your mother's words—that he was, quote, a very understanding person, unquote.'

She said nothing, gritting her teeth in her effort to remain taut. It was becoming uncomfortable and she longed to relax, but that would constitute a victory for him. They would be touching again.

Still tense, she leant forward to pick up a magazine from the low table in front of them. A flick through it showed her advertisements for large country houses, for Rolls-Royces and mink coats. The magazine represented a world that was entirely foreign to her. Her impulse was to replace the magazine on the table, but although its contents did not interest her, she pretended that it did. It formed a barrier between herself and the man beside her.

The magazine was taken from her and replaced on the table. 'Did your mother never teach you good manners?'

Lisette coloured deeply, but bit back the apology which sprang to her lips. She would continue to deny this man's domination for as long as she had strength. Whether that strength would need to be mental or physical, she could not at that stage in their acquaintance decide.

'Tell me about your work, Lisette.' He settled himself more comfortably, folding his arms.

It was no use, she just had to relax. Her present position was untenable for the length of time which he seemed prepared to spend in that lounge. One by one, her muscles loosened until his arm was against hers again, his hip, his leg—was it her imagination, or was he closer than before?

She shrugged—and regretted it. It had caused friction between them, setting her nerves tingling, sending through her stiff body sensations that were quite alien to her, feelings that she hated because they brought the colour to her cheeks. This man both embarrassed and annoyed her, but because she was playing a part—that of a worldly business woman—she must tolerate his company and his ways as if she were completely unaffected by them.

'Well,' he said, unfolding his arms and putting one across the back of the settee behind her, 'what do you do with your working day, besides acting as your own inquiry desk attendant and your own secretary?'

She steeled herself to tolerate the touch of his hand as it drooped down over her shoulder. 'I attend fashion shows, watching for trends in footwear. I go to displays of shoes by manufacturers. They're often held in hotels and our own designer usually goes with me, looking for ideas for our own products.'

'Go on,' he said, 'I'm interested. Maybe you could teach *me* a thing or two, after all!'

She smiled. 'I doubt if I could teach you anything at all.'

'You'd be surprised,' he said laconically.

'Our buyer,' she went on, 'goes round buying skins and a lot of the materials used in shoe manufacture. We supply multiple and chain stores besides smaller retailers. Store buyers ask if we could make a special line in shoes for their own requirements. We—we try to establish good relations with store buyers.' How long could she go on without boring him? A glance told her she was a long way from that point. For the first time he was giving her his entire attention. He had forgotten she was feminine! Her heart leapt. For a few moments at least, she was his equal.

'Sometimes,' she continued, 'they want something to fit into their next range and would we please produce a suitable design? Our designer talks over the style with them and does his best to comply with their needs.'

Lisette stopped and he looked at her inquiringly. 'Go on,' he urged. 'Tell me some more.'

She laughed and her heartbeats quickened at the sudden warmth in his eyes. He had turned from a small boy wanting to hear the rest of the 'bedtime story' into a mature man with very male instincts and desires.

Hurriedly she continued, 'The soles of our shoes are injection moulded. They're synthetic, not leather.'

'So I gathered. You told me you didn't handle leather much.'

So he had remembered what she had said at the Chamber of Trade reception!

'That's true, but we do use leather sometimes, in addition to synthetics. We use brush-off leathers, suede, pigskins and cowhide. We buy from the tannery, sometimes even full sides of hide. We usually use synthetic linings, though.' She added, glancing at him again, 'Something we've discovered is that feet are more or less the same the world over.'

He laughed. 'Which probably means that a fact like that would affect the size of the last?'

She nodded. 'They're made of beech or hornbeam or, these days, maple.'

'How many pairs of shoes do you produce?'

She shrugged. 'Five, ten, even fifteen thousand pairs

a week. Not as much, I suppose, as the really big shoe manufacturers turn out. But then we're only a small family business.'

'Beset by problems.'

It was a statement made, she was sure, to provoke a revelation by her of the secrets he seemed to have guessed she was hiding. However, she stayed silent.

He asked, 'Where did you learn all you've been telling me?'

'Picked it up as I went along.'

'Clever you!'

The sarcasm brought her head round. 'I've done my best. I've struggled to keep the firm afloat.'

'And now it's sinking, slowly but surely drowning?'

So it had been yet another ruse to get her to reveal the extent of their troubles. 'Did I say so?' she challenged.

'My word, you're a hard nut to crack! You've certainly earned my respect, Miss Baird.'

She turned away, experiencing a strange, unnerving feeling of disappointment. His respect. Was that all he had for her? But what else had she wanted? Admiration for her womanhood, her feminine attractions? Hadn't she wanted to be accepted on equal terms with him? How perverse could she get? she wondered miserably.

His nearness was stirring within her a disquieting response. His hand had found its way under the jacket to the bareness of her shoulder and was gently caressing her skin. It had even, in an intimate way, slid beneath the shoulder strap of her dress. The caressing action was invoking from her depths feelings she had never before experienced.

They worried her, these feelings, because slowly but decisively they were beginning to override her intellect, blurring the edges of her powers of reason. They were burrowing like potholers beneath her rational thought to unknown areas of her personality. Great underground palaces were being opened up, Aladdin's caves of longing and desire, holding unbelievable promises of pleasure and fulfilment.

Her head came round quickly. 'Please,' she said. Her cheeks were flushed, her eyes showing her distress.

No other words were necessary. Slowly the hand was withdrawn, to rest again along the back of the settee. Slowly, too, Lisette's feelings subsided to their normal, dormant state. She breathed steadily again.

'Shall we go?' His voice was without expression. So he had been trying her out, he had been on a voyage of discovery of his own. How far would she allow a man to go? Her plea had been the answer. No touching, no physical contact, no intimacy of any kind, not even a sharing of thoughts and troubles.

Rosco stood before her, looking down. She was intensely aware of the height of him, the easy manner, the wealth which sat astride his well-suited shoulders like a child being given a pick-a-back by his father.

The thought had her tensing. This man a father. The simile had been no accident, it had been her subconscious mind playing tricks ... The father of whose children? Certainly, most certainly not hers. 'A woman for every mood,' he had said so cynically about his private life. She, Lisette Baird, had fitted into none of them.

He took her home and pulled up in front of the house, which was in a cul-de-sac. He had spoken little on the way and had seemed preoccupied. Lisette had swung her coat from her shoulders on leaving the hotel. She pulled the edges together.

There was a chill in the air. Whether it was the cool spring temperature or the atmosphere in the car, she could not tell. If he was put out, she could not understand why. Maybe it was her failure to respond to his subtle yet unmistakable approaches, man to woman, in which case it must be disappointment and not anger that had given him an air of remoteness.

'Thank——' Before she could finish, he had moved, turning in his seat and pulling her face round.

He was urging her across to him and, since it would have hurt if she had resisted, she went. With that same hand he encompassed her throat and lowered his mouth to her lips. In her surprise, she did not repel him. He did not lift his mouth and the longer it stayed over hers, the more the feeling of liking the warmth and controlled demand it contained began to grow within her, like a new life clamouring and kicking to be born.

Terrified at the way this—this thing she had harboured inside her without even knowing it was increasing, enlarging, threatening to take her over altogether, this—this—surely it couldn't be *passion*?—was conquering her willpower to such an extent that she felt no wish to pull away, her hands came alive and lifted to grasp his sleeve, tugging his hand away.

It was like hitting the side of a mountain to make it topple over. So her palms found his forehead and pushed with all their strength. It was not her action which stopped him so much as the repulsion he probably reasoned she must have experienced at his touch.

He lifted his head, releasing her mouth which continued to throb with the remembered pressure of his lips. It had, for him, been a chaste kiss—that much Lisette had guessed. He had not even tried to force her lips apart.

He was angry, she could see by the way his eyes glittered in the yellow light from the lamps which curved high over their heads, lighting the road.

'What's wrong?' he jeered. 'Isn't your boy-friend "understanding" enough to allow another man to kiss his beloved?'

She was angry, too, but she could not explain even to herself the reason for that anger. 'Is that your usual way,' she hit back, her voice quivering strangely, 'of exacting payment from your female companions for the money—not to say the valuable time—you've expended on them in taking them out for a meal? Because if it is, don't ask me out again!'

'Don't worry,' he answered, 'no such invitations will be forthcoming. I don't enjoy the company of spitfires, vixens, cold-blooded she-cats.'

'I'm sorry, so *very* sorry, for not fitting in with any of your *moods*.' Had she been sarcastic enough to hurt him?

It seemed not. He gave a short, caustic laugh. 'You, fit in with any of my moods? That's as likely as the moon colliding with the sun. Not even if I were in a mood of black despair would I ring *you* for comfort and release.'

He had found her most vulnerable spot and she wanted to cry out with the pain. Even if she could not give a man love or arouse his desire, she was still a woman, and at the very least could offer him comfort. That had always been her belief, the one piece of self-knowledge that had been her prop and her main source of the small amount of self-confidence she possessed. With one blow he had knocked it clean away.

Bewilderment weighted down her mind and body, keeping her sitting in the passenger seat when she should have opened the door and got out, taking with her the small piece of dignity he had allowed her to keep. Why were they quarrelling with such venom? To him it had been an evening—one of so many— spent with a woman. To her it had been a business appointment. How had it deteriorated into a personal conflict of unimaginable bitterness?

'Tell me something.' He broke the silence. 'In spite of all you've told me this evening about Baird Shoes, about its methods and the way it supplies the requirements of shoe shops and department stores, the firm is still in financial trouble? Is that correct?'

Lisette nodded.

'Am I permitted to ask how it all came about?'

Falling demand, out-of-date machinery, lack of investment on my father's part ... No, she could not tell him these things.

She sighed and shook her head as resignedly as possible. 'We'll manage somehow.' It seemed he was unconvinced by her piece of acting.

'So you won't answer my question?' Lisette was silent. 'In spite of the fact,' he persisted, 'that you asked me for a loan?'

She turned on him. 'I did not ask you for a loan!'

He said slowly, deliberately, 'It wasn't advice you wanted, you said, it was money. What's that if not a request for a loan?'

'A statement of fact, that's all. If you misinterpreted my statement, that's your fault, not mine.'

'So you wouldn't accept it even if I offered you one?'

Her heart leapt, but subsided immediately. It was out of the question to accept any help from Rosco Hamden, after all he had said about Baird Shoes.

'Go to my bank manager, you said,' she replied as steadily as her turbulent emotions would allow. 'That was your advice. So you won't offer me a loan, will you?'

'No, Miss Baird, I won't.' He spoke so quietly, a quiver of fear ran through her.

Be nice to him, her mother had pleaded. But she had been more unpleasant to him than she had ever been to any man.

CHAPTER FOUR

LISETTE did not tell her mother much about the evening she had spent with Rosco Hamden. She hardened herself to tolerate the bright look of hope that greeted her as she entered the house. When the inevitable question came, 'Is he going to help us?' she was ready with a slow shake of the head.

Her mother's look of intense disappointment had almost been her undoing, and if her mother had not turned away, saying, 'I'll make some coffee,' Lisette was sure she would have burst into tears in her mother's arms.

Now she was at her desk on the morning of a day three weeks later. She had assumed that during that time Rosco Hamden had returned to his scene of big business and industrial complexes. Rightly so, it seemed, judging by the information her mother had gleaned from his recent host, Stanley Burlington.

'No idea when he's returning,' Stanley had said on the telephone. 'In fact, he left suddenly, a day earlier than expected. He didn't give a reason.'

When she heard the news, Lisette's heart had dived. Had it been her behaviour when he had taken her out? Or had he taken himself with all possible speed from the threatened involvement with a doomed, pigmy-sized company called Baird Shoes?

That morning she had been with the firm's designer and supervisor, Bernard Browning, to a Shoe Fair at a famous London hotel. 'Looking for trends,' she had told her mother. The phrase had about it a ring of optimism, implying that there was a future for the firm, that it must look ahead, as the Shoe Fair was doing, to the autumn styles.

Whether those trends for which they were looking would ever be fashioned in the Baird factory into tangible objects, shoes to hold in one's hand, Lisette had grave doubts. So did Bob Farrell, who looked after the money side of the business.

Bob had taken Lisette out a number of times. They would go to see a film or to London by train to a show. They had had early evening meals and in the theatre, they would sit in the third most expensive seats—sometimes, as a special treat, in the second most expensive.

Bob, being an employee of the firm and like the rest of the workers, underpaid but accepting the fact, did not have a great deal of spare money for such treats. Often Lisette would insist on paying her share. If Bob's loyalty to the firm—and Lisette—had not been so unshakeable, he could have earned far more as the employee of another company. He knew this, but still he stayed on, and his dedication to his work and the firm almost moved Lisette to tears.

But if Bob had started kissing her with a deeper feeling, she knew she would not have cared for the experience, either on its own merits or in the inevitable comparison with the kiss which Rosco Hamden had bestowed upon her with a kind of considerate ruthlessness—if there were such a thing—after he had taken her out.

Bob was affectionate yet made few demands on her. They talked and walked together and she felt his equal in every way. They had held hands, kissed on the cheek and nothing more. And that was exactly how Lisette intended their friendship to continue.

Earlier that morning, while she and Bernard Browning had wandered round the Shoe Fair, Lisette had played a game of 'let's pretend'. She had done it partly to boost her own flagging morale, and partly to reassure Bernard that all was well within the firm. His own enthusiasm had helped to carry her along. It had enabled her to disguise the apprehension about future demand which, as the owner of the firm, she was forced to hide from the employees.

She had also known that that afternoon she would be going to see the company's bank manager about the uncertain future of the business. Lisette hoped—it was, she admitted, probably a vain hope—that the 'family' aspect, the fact that he had known her father—might help along her case for an extension of the period and the amount of the overdraft they already had from the bank.

As she mounted the steps to the bank entrance, and told the girl at the inquiries desk that she had an appointment to see Mr Jackson, the manager, her courage nearly failed her. Deep down she knew she had little chance of achieving her object.

When the interview was over and she was descending the steps, Lisette knew that her instinct had been right. No loan was forthcoming from the bank, and that was final. Before any further help could be extended to the firm, she had been told, the overdraft would have to be reduced. After all that Lisette had been forced to tell him, Mr Jackson, sympathetic though he was, had had grave doubts about the future of the business.

When Bob heard about the unsuccessful interview with the bank manager, he said, 'There's this contract with Carriers of London, Lisette. If they cancel it as they're threatening to do, we've really had it. Now we know the worst from the bank, we'll have to do something. I suggest you phone Carriers and have a talk with their chief buyer. It's a man, so,' he gave a smile, 'it might help if you use your feminine charms.'

Lisette made a face. There it was again—womanly

charms! 'I haven't got any, Bob,' she said wearily. If she had, she thought, she would have charmed both the bank manager and Rosco Hamden into giving her everything she wanted in order to save the firm.

Something told her, however, that the chief executive of Electro-Magnetic Universal would not have been satisfied with mere 'charms'. To have extracted any promise, let alone financial assistance from such a man, he would have wanted something she was simply not prepared to give—everything of herself, both her body and her soul.

She reached for the phone. 'I can but try. What's Carriers' number?'

Bob watched her dial the famous department store in the heart of London. Then he sat back and listened to the conversation, showing neither disappointment nor optimism at the result.

Lisette sighed as she replaced the telephone. 'They wouldn't give me any promises. But at least the shoe buyer's coming here tomorrow to talk things over.'

That night, as she lay in bed, she had been unable to sleep for thinking. Thinking about Rosco Hamden, about the difficulties facing Baird Shoes, about its doubtful future and about the anxiety which she knew her mother was doing her best to conceal beneath a veneer of smiling optimism.

Lisette could not get Rosco Hamden out of her mind. She tried calling him arrogant and selfish, unfeeling and hard, but it was no use. It was the feel of his hand on her skin that she could not forget, the kiss with which he had tested her reaction to a man's eternal question where a woman—any woman, for a man like him—was concerned.

Nor could she forget the way she had repulsed him, no doubt hurting his pride, being bitter and recriminating instead of allowing him to kiss her as the pleasantest way a woman could find of saying 'thank you'.

But his kiss had not been 'pleasant'. It had stirred her so deeply, considerate though it had been, that it had frightened her because of what it had succeeded in doing. It had shown her that, just beneath the surface, was a warm-hearted woman clamouring to be recognised, fighting to break free of the constraints she had imposed over the years.

If only she had been a son. She could not forget that overheard regret. Ever since she had heard those murmured words between her parents, she had done her best to try to prove, both to them and to herself, that, depite the fact that she was a woman, she possessed enough drive and ability to rival that of any man.

Lisette and Bob entertained the shoe buyer of Carriers of London to lunch at the town's best hotel. They knew they were wasting their time and their money. He had already looked round the factory, seen the out-of-date machinery, inspected the range of styles Baird Shoes were offering and had shaken his head.

'I'm sorry, Miss Baird,' the man called Farrow had said. 'This fashion may be right for now, but it's on the way out. The trend began to change at the turn of the year.' With a slightly reproving look at Bernard Browning, 'Your designer here should have spotted it at the fashion shows and shoe fairs. I could see it coming last autumn.'

'But he saw it, too,' Lisette had hastened to assure him. 'It was just that we couldn't turn out the designs——' She had stopped as Bob gave a quick shake of his head. He had cut off the tell-tale confession. 'To meet the deadline,' Lisette finished lamely.

'I'll alter the design,' Bernard had offered eagerly, seizing a pad and pencil. 'How about something like——?'

Mr Farrow had shaken his head. 'Too late, my friend. By the time you're in a position to supply the goods,' looking round disparagingly at the machinery and speaking over the noise, 'the fashion will have changed again. Invest some capital in the business, Miss Baird, get it refurbished with better equipment. Then you'll be able to compete with the giants and satisfy our requirements at the same time.'

When Mr Farrow had gone, Lisette and Bob returned to the factory and sat despondently in Lisette's office. The lump in Lisette's throat would not go, however much she swallowed, but the tears did not trickle through. Her self-control held. She did not give way to the feminine weakness of crying when presented with a crisis, however much she longed to do so.

She picked up an empty ashtray from her desk top and turned it round and round in her hands. Her thoughts were going in circles, too.

'Invest our capital, he said,' she remarked bitterly, 'when there's none to invest. Borrow from the bank, Rosco Hamden said, when there's none available for us to borrow. Pay back some of the overdraft, the bank manager said, then I might be able to help.' Her lips trembled but she stilled them, even managing a weak smile. 'It's ironic, isn't it, Bob?'

In reply he stood beside her and she looked up at him. He kissed her on the lips and she did not repel him as she had Rosco Hamden. But she felt nothing at all.

Bob resumed his seat. 'You'll have to face it, Lisette, and so will your mother. It's bankruptcy.'

'Couldn't we—sell up?'

'Lisette,' as though speaking to a child, 'who would want to buy? How much are the assets worth? And you can count them, anyway, on the fingers of one hand.'

'My mother,' Lisette whispered, 'what will she say? What will she do?'

Bob shook his head, looked at his employer with compassion and said gently, 'She'll have to be told, you know.'

Lisette nodded tearfully and the bell rang throughout the factory, signifying the end of a working day.

'There's only one thing we can do, Lisette,' said Evelyn Baird, leaning forward from the depths of the large armchair.

Lisette was sitting, legs under her, on the long-piled rug in front of the electric log fire which stood in the hearth. She stared into its imitation flames as if they held the answer to all their problems. But the fickle flicker danced and glowed, giving out promises as false as the flames themselves.

'There's nothing left for us to do, Mother,' she said with a sigh.

A short silence followed, then, as if she had found the necessary courage to speak, Evelyn said, 'Rosco Hamden. He'll help us.'

Lisette swung round. 'Rosco Hamden? Are you crazy, Mother? He's already stated categorically that he won't lift a finger to help us. He told me he's not in business to act as a money-lender. He told me——'

'Lisette, dear,' her mother's voice was tense and urgent, 'it's absolutely imperative that we do something to try to save ourselves. We can't let any chance go by. There'—she looked at her daughter warily—'there must be a softer side to him you can reach. You're— you're a sweet young girl, dear. You must know how——'

Lisette felt sickened. Would her mother hold nothing sacred in her efforts to maintain her high standard of living? 'What do you want me to do,' she asked bitterly, 'go to Rosco Hamden and—and give him whatever he might want of me to keep the family business on its feet, tottering though it may be? It's

71

no real sacrifice these days, is it, because so many girls have no scruples where that sort of thing is concerned.'

'*Lisette!*' Her mother turned pale and her eyes moistened. 'How can you say such a thing!'

Lisette, immediately contrite, uncurled herself and went to her mother's side. 'I'm sorry, Mother,' she wound her arms round her mother's neck and sat on the arm of the chair. 'I didn't mean to hurt you, but I've thought and thought and there seems no way out.' I've stayed awake at nights thinking in circles ...'

Mrs Baird patted her eyes. 'It's a bad time for all of us, dear, so don't think I don't know what you're going through. But *please*, Lisette, don't let it make you bitter.'

'I feel I've failed you, Mother.'

'Nonsense! You're the most wonderful daughter any woman could wish to have. And I absolutely *know* you'll think of some way.' She turned appealing eyes to her daughter's face. 'Lisette, there—there is the way I suggested.' A long, hurtful silence. 'You could at least try, couldn't you?'

Her mother's pleading, the unaccustomed diffidence and uncertainty, moved Lisette to her depths. Go and see Rosco Hamden ... How could she sink her pride and do as her mother wished?

Resolution came in the sleepless hours of the night. She would seek an interview with Rosco Hamden. It would take courage to go back on her word, to retract her defiant declaration that she would never ask him for help. It was important, she decided, dressing after a restless night, not to think of him as the chief executive of a world-renowned electronics organisation.

But, she thought hopelessly, if she tried to reduce him to the status of 'a mere man', it inevitably brought with it pictures in her mind of his kissing her, caressing her ...

However she had privately decided to look upon

him, whether as man or tycoon, when she telephoned Universal House for an appointment to see the head of the company, she was reminded with some force of his position.

'Have you an appointment?' the girl asked brightly. 'No? Then I'm sorry, it's out of the question to see Mr Hamden today. In any case, you won't be able to see Mr Hamden. His deputy, maybe, or the deputy's assistant, but Mr Hamden does not see members of the public, unless——'

'Unless.' That was the word she must hang on to as though her life depended on it. What should she say? 'This is a personal matter'? But that was not true. It was business and there could be no argument about it.

'Mr Hamden knows me personally,' she said. 'He——'

'Madam,' the girl said with forced patience, 'Mr Hamden knows many people personally. May I ask exactly what it was you wanted to see him about?'

'*Are you his bodyguard?*' Lisette nearly shouted, but with an immense effort contained her frustration.

'May I speak to his secretary, then? Just a word, that's all I want. *Please.*'

'Oh,' Lisette heard a sigh, 'all right. What name shall I say?' Lisette told her. 'Just a moment, please.'

A click, a short silence, another click, then a pleasant voice inquired, 'Mr Hamden's secretary. Can I help you?'

Lisette could not believe her good fortune. She was within a secretary's distance of the man she wanted. Of course, that could either mean the quick, skilful brush-off, or with luck, entry to the lofty heights of the world of the head of Electro-Magnetic Universal.

'I—I think you can. I mean,' a quick, embarrassed correction, 'I hope you can. I would like to make an appointment to see Mr Hamden.'

'I see,' was the encouraging answer. 'Can you tell me

your business, Miss Baird?' Lisette's courage nearly failed her. 'Unfortunately, Mr Hamden can't see everyone who wants to see *him*, so perhaps someone else might be able to help you without bothering Mr Hamden.'

Lisette began to despair. 'I'm afraid that's impossible. You see,' she found that her hand was clutching the stem of the receiver hard enough to break a less well-made piece of equipment, 'it's—it's business.'

'I gathered that,' the girl answered with a touch of amusement.

'P-personal business.'

'Oh.' A long pause. Now what was the secretary thinking? It became obvious as the girl said, 'Would you like me to put you through to Mr Hamden himself?'

Lisette's heart leapt. The break-through at last! She replied with undisguised eagerness, 'Oh, yes, please!'

A few moments later a curt voice said, 'Miss Baird?'

Her heart leapt for a second time—then dropped like a stone. It was not Rosco Hamden speaking, it was the chief executive of Emu products and no mistake! It was a disembodied voice she was talking to, not a man with warm, demanding lips and keen, sardonic eyes.

Like a re-run of a television play she remembered their words as they had parted the evening he had taken her to dinner. *So you won't offer me a loan, will you?* she had challenged.

No, Miss Baird, I won't, he had answered. And she had been afraid. Had she known even then, deep in her heart, what the future might hold?

Impatiently, his voice came again. 'Miss Baird, are you there?' My time is valuable, he was saying, my time is money.

'Yes,' faintly. 'I'm sorry. Is it possible to—to see you, Mr Hamden?'

There was a hard silence, then, 'Before I answer, I

74

should like to know why you want to see me.'

Lisette clenched her teeth, closed her eyes and said, 'It's about business, Mr Hamden.'

'What business?'

'Mine, Mr Hamden. Mine and my mother's.'

The repeated taps of a pencil answered her. 'I see.' More taps, then they ceased. A decision had been reached. 'I'll put you back to my secretary. She'll give you a date and time.' No chance to thank him, he had gone.

'Miss Baird?' The pleasant voice of the secretary was soothing. An appointment was fixed for two days ahead. After lunch, two-thirty prompt, the girl said.

Lisette did not bother to eat and the coffee she ordered at the station buffet she drank with difficulty. She had known nervousness before, but nothing as intense as this.

In the waiting room into which Rosco Hamden's secretary had shown her, she looked with blank eyes through the various quality magazines which lay about the room. Her eyes strayed. If this was a foretaste of the top man's office, then his must be luxurious indeed.

She had arrived early and now the hands of her watch crept slowly to the half hour. Impatient with anxiety, she thrust aside the glossy pages and went to the window. The view over London was breathtaking—if she had had any breath left inside her to be taken. Her lungs felt stifled, her legs stiff, her brain petrified into a solid mass. Coherent thought was impossible. Her driving instinct was to escape, but even if she did turn coward and run away, she knew that the inevitable would catch up with her.

'I'm a long, long way up, aren't I, Miss Baird?' She swung round at the familiar, mocking voice. 'How did you ever manage to reach me?'

He stood at a communicating door which she had

not noticed. He was the same yet different, as tall, as distinguished, as taunting; yet more remote, forbidding, his physique more powerful, his keen eyes more probing, if that were possible. His body, still though it was, hinted at a greater vigour. In his own surroundings, he was altogether more intimidating, and Lisette wanted to run for her life.

While her eyes searched in vain for a chink in the executive crust in which he was encased and through which she could perceive not even a hint of human understanding, his had been busy stripping from her the veneer of brittle sophistication in which she had mentally covered herself. By the glinting mockery in his wandering gaze, he had without doubt found the uncertain, vulnerable young girl for which he had been looking.

It was no use, she could not win against his greater experience, his skill in reducing an opponent to size. He was not head of a great international organisation for nothing. She knew as she returned his look and just before her eyes fell away from his that he had reduced *her* from business executive to inferior womanhood.

'Come into my parlour, Miss Baird. I'm delighted to see you. What brings you into the rarefied atmosphere of London's world of commerce and industry?'

Clichés, the jargon of business host to guest, the strong to the weak to make them feel at ease.

'I came to see you, Mr Hamden,' she said, passing in front of him and holding herself tense as their bodies touched in the doorway, 'on—on a business matter.'

'Pity,' he said teasingly, 'I hoped it was my magnetic charm that had drawn you all this way to see me.'

She scarcely heard him, having caught her breath at what she saw. It was not an office into which she had walked, but a great room furnished with settees and armchairs, low, glass-topped tables, aluminium, long-stemmed ashtrays and a carpet with pile as thick as

76

meadow grass. On the walls were modern paintings, on circular tables spring flowers were massed in decorative pottery and glass containers.

'Not a desk in sight, Miss Baird,' she heard him say. 'Not a swivel chair, nor a highly polished surface on which, I believe you once accused, I rested my lazy feet.' His memory was embarrassingly good.

She could find no words with which to answer. If he had not intimidated her on sight, his work place, if such a name could be given to it, would have demolished any remaining shell of self-confidence.

'An executive suite *par excellence*, is it not, Miss Baird?' He motioned her to a chair which she gladly occupied. 'No shelves with a line of learned books leaning drunkenly against each other. No folders strewn over the floor, no chair with one leg shorter than the other three legs and from which I have to sweep a pile of papers in order to let you sit down.'

'No ancient electric kettle,' she responded, 'no chipped mug from which to drink your instant coffee. You've made your point, Mr Hamden.' A smile flickered like a faulty light bulb, then went out completely.

'If that was a hint, I'll take it.' He leant forward from the armchair into which he had dropped, flicked a switch on an intercom on a table beside him and said, 'Coffee for two, Pamela.'

'It wasn't a hint, Mr Hamden,' said Lisette. 'I don't give hints.' She tried another smile, but nothing happened. The mechanism was out of action.

'No,' he took her up, 'you come right out with it—I know you well enough to be aware of that. I still bear some of your scars.'

She looked down at her twisted fingers. 'I'm sorry.'

'You're not, are you?' She looked up, surprised, seeing his sardonic smile. 'You're pleased. There are times when you hit hard.'

'You don't exactly pull your own punches!'

A brief silence, then he said, 'Born of the instinct for self-preservation. It's something one learns quickly in the rat race, the commercial jungle I've been roaming in since my early twenties. It's something you'll have to learn one of these days, when that business you own begins to thrive again and you start challenging your competitors in the world of shoe fashion.'

This was the opening for which she had hoped. She opened her mouth to speak the words she had rehearsed—but nothing happened. Fear had tied her brain into knots.

There was a buzz and Rosco flicked a switch. 'Coffee, Mr Hamden. Shall I bring it in?'

'Please, Pamela.' The girl entered carrying a salver on which there were two attractive brown pottery cups and saucers, silver pot and cream jug. She placed the salver on a low table which she moved between them. An assortment of biscuits lay on a small silver dish. It was food of a kind and it made Lisette acutely aware of the hungry void in her stomach.

Rosco invited her to pour. As she did so, he relaxed in his armchair, legs crossed, arms resting loosely on the sides. His eyes were narrow and watchful. Lisette wished he would speak—anything to break the intense silence.

Since the windows were treble-glazed and the executive suite was on the eleventh floor, no sound of traffic penetrated into the room. There was only the clatter that Lisette made as she placed the coffee pot back on the tray.

'Black,' said Rosco, and Lisette jumped as if it had been a gun shot. He laughed. 'Good grief, you must be on edge! Relax, Lisette.' He leaned forward to take his coffee. 'I don't eat little girls.'

'No,' she replied, adding cream to her coffee, 'only little firms like mine.'

His smile hardened for a passing second, then his relaxed manner returned. 'Drink your coffee with plenty of sugar. It might help to sweeten you.'

This was a bad start. She remembered her mother's anxious kiss on the cheek as they had parted on the doorstep. 'Do your best,' she had said, 'for all our sakes.'

Lisette did her best—and produced a brilliant smile. Its effect on her host was to bring him forward in his chair with the apparent object of narrowing the gap between them.

'I'm really very sweet,' Lisette said.

'Really?' Did she detect a dry note? 'I must taste you some time.' He watched the colour creep over her cheeks. 'Last time, our contact was over too quickly for me to make a proper assessment.' If only his smile were genuine, she thought, without the touch of cruelty which pulled at his lips.

She was wading into deep water. Before she floundered, she must return to the safety of the shore.

'Biscuit?' She shook her head, longing for sustenance, but knowing it would taste like sand. 'Too much lunch?' She hesitated, then nodded. If she told him she had had no food, he would regard it as a weakness, one he would latch on to and with it bring her down. 'Did you lunch alone?' he asked. Another pause, then she nodded. 'Lost your tongue?' He was genuinely smiling and she laughed. 'You're beautiful when you laugh. You should do it more often, Lisette. You could wring a man's last penny out of him if you laughed like that.'

He replaced his cup and saucer on the salver and Lisette put hers beside it. For the first time that day she felt able to relax.

'Why did you come to see me?'

The question caught her completely off guard. Her set piece escaped her, she could not remember a word. Much as she hated his cunning device to put his opponent at his—or her—ease, then fell that opponent with one blow before the battle began, she had to admire it.

There was nothing she could do now except rise to his challenge. She picked herself up mentally, flexed the muscles of her mind and said,

'To ask you for a loan.'

If he staggered infinitesimally at the straightness of her punch, he did not show it. That faint smile which had irritated her in the past manifested itself around his lips.

'So.' He looked her over, noting the midnight blue cord velvet suit, the simple white blouse, the matching blue shoes and handbag. 'The worker-director, ex-librarian has had to come crawling to me on her hands and knees after all?'

Lisette gritted her teeth. There was no room for emotion here. This was the world of industry and commerce. The 'rat race', he had called it. She was in it up to her neck. She was fighting for the family business—and her mother's creature comforts, the way of life her father had bequeathed.

What happened to Lisette Baird did not really matter, but what happened to her mother certainly did. This man could fling insults like hard-packed snowballs and when they hit her, no matter how they stung, she would not flinch. She looked at him, her face pale, her head high. Yes, another was coming her way.

'So you want someone to pull you out, to put it a little crudely. You want someone to throw you a life-line and pull you out of the mess into which you've got the management of Baird Shoes?'

'You can hurl insults at me until midnight and beyond, Mr Hamden. You still won't deflect me from my course. I intend to save the family business.'

He sat motionless for a few seconds, then tapped his fingertips on the chair arms as if he were playing the piano. With impatient energy he leant forward, took up a biscuit and tossed it into Lisette's lap. He grinned. 'Makes a change from insults.'

Then he took another biscuit and bit through its brittleness, chewing it thoughtfully. He noticed the biscuit lying untouched in Lisette's lap. 'Go on, eat it,' he urged, smiling, 'let's chew the cud together.'

The industrialist seemed to have slipped away, leaving in command the man—approachable, almost human—who had visited the factory, drunk coffee from a chipped mug, taken her out, fondled her, kissed her.

Lisette picked up the biscuit and ate it. To have put it from her would have been to have conceded him a small but definite victory. Anyway, she was hungry.

He stood, brushing away the crumbs and thrusting his hands into his trouser pockets. The action revealed lean hips, the belted waistline of an active man.

He towered above her, the executive glint back in his eyes. 'Tell me about this young man, Bob Farrell. Is he a trained accountant?'

If only she could have told him 'yes'. She had to shake her head. 'He came with me from the library.'

'Good God, so there are two librarians running the business, not just one?'

'He's extremely intelligent, with an excellent brain——'

'Of course,' Rosco broke in, his lips twisting cynically, 'you would praise him. He's your boy-friend.'

'Allow me some managerial insight!' she cried, roused to fury by his taunt. 'At least allow me the ability to judge an employee impartially, whatever my imagined relationship with him might be.'

An eyebrow rose. 'Imagined?'

'We're no more than friends.'

The broad shoulders shrugged. 'It's a start. Friendship between couples contemplating marriage is not to be dismissed lightly.'

81

Lisette ignored the sarcasm she had come to accept. 'I may be female——'

The cool eyes a long way above hers appraised, the curving lips mocked. 'No doubt about it, Miss Baird.'

'I may be female,' she persisted, 'but I am able to separate my emotions from my reason.'

'Are you? I have yet to meet the woman—a real woman, as you are, not the half-man kind—who can distinguish between emotion and reason, let alone separate them. And even if they can,' he went on, ignoring her attempts to answer back, 'they always blur the edges of thought and discussion with their imprecise and muddled approach to everything. With them, emotion always runs into reason and curdles it——'

She broke in fiercely, 'Your hatred of women curdles *you*. You're obnoxious!'

The eyes, so cool moments ago, flared into life. 'It might be as well to remind you that you are trying to get a loan out of me. Diplomacy and tact are considered two of the essential ingredients of management technique. But then you wouldn't know,' he derided, 'not having received even the elements of managerial training. You're probably running the shoe factory as if it were a beauty salon.'

She sprang to her feet. 'I came to ask you for a loan, Mr Hamden,' she stormed, 'not ridicule and insults.'

'You've just insulted me, Miss Baird. You called me obnoxious.'

'Which makes us quits,' she spat back.

'Alas for you,' he said silkily, 'it does not. I have the money you want so badly. That makes us very unequal indeed.'

He had floored her and she drooped, not knowing where to look or what to do.

'You're out for the count, Miss Baird,' he jeered. 'You just can't win against me. Do you concede victory?' She wanted to tear that tormenting, enigmatic smile from his face.

'No!' she choked.

'But you'll have to. You see, I hold the trump card. Let me put it this way. It's not in my company's interest to invest money in something that is unprofitable. So,' he paused as if to give his pronouncement greater emphasis, 'you're not getting your loan.'

She sank into the chair again, elbow on the arm, head in hand.

'You once said,' he walked slowly towards her, 'that I'd be the last man you'd ever ask for financial help.' He was so near his jacket brushed her hair as she sat, supporting her head. 'Does it pain you to be reminded of that?'

'You *are* the last man,' she whispered.

Fingers trailed the back of her neck and she shivered, unable to tolerate his touch because she hated him so much for his intractability, yet at the same time loving the touch of him. *Loving?* The shiver grew into a shudder and he stopped. And she wanted him to go on and on caressing her ...

Aghast at the thoughts that were chasing in circles round her brain, she drew herself in until every muscle was rigid. He was so near and her head so low, if she opened her eyes she could see his thighs, the whole inviting, irresistible masculinity of him ...

'Have you tried the bank manager as I suggested?'

She nodded. Was he relenting? Had he now reduced her to a sufficiently low state in his—and her own—estimation that he was satisfied?

'What happened?' Rosco asked.

'Like you, he refused a loan.' A quivering sigh escaped her, telling him, she thought despairingly, everything he might want to know about her inner torment. 'My father, some time before he died, had negotiated an overdraft in an attempt to rescue the family business from extinction.'

He waited for more. When it did not come, he asked, 'What went wrong?'

'Can't you guess?' she said tonelessly. 'Instead of ploughing all the bank loan into the business, that is, replacing the old machinery with modern equipment, building new premises, or even patching up what already existed, he spent most of it on jewellery and clothes for my mother, the house, holidays, drink.'

'So, even before you took over, the firm was going downhill?' She nodded.

He crouched down and lifted her chin, forcing her head up. 'Why didn't you tell me this before?'

She moved her head and his fingers lost contact with her chin. She shrugged. 'Pride.'

He straightened to his formidable height. It seemed that once again she had offended his professional instincts. '*Pride*, where business is concerned and where it concerns the future well-being of dozens of working people, of customers, creditors and bankers? It's what I've been saying, isn't it? Trust a woman to drag emotion into her business life!'

She stood to challenge him, trying to disregard the strange weakness of her legs. She wanted this man to speak softly to her, gently, lovingly, not deride her every time the opportunity arose. She wanted to speak lovingly to this man, feel his arms about her possessively, kissing her fears and tears into extinction under the reassurance of his love ...

The room spun at what was happening to her and she put a hand to her head. He offered no assistance, asked no questions as to whether anything was wrong. She found renewed strength in resentment that he could be so unfeeling and said,

'You speak of pride as a *womanly emotion*? To me, pride has no gender. It's something every man and woman should feel about *something*. In my case, it was family pride. You seem to forget, my mother is also an interested party, being co-director of Baird Shoes.' Rosco did not speak in the short pause. 'There was also my—self-respect.'

This time he did begin to speak, to remonstrate by the look in his eyes and to castigate, Lisette was sure, but she held up her hand. 'It's all right. I have no self-respect left. I lost the last shreds of it when I forced myself to come and see you.'

Hopelessly she turned to find her handbag, then faced him squarely. 'Thank you for seeing me. Thank you for spending some of the profits of Electro-Magnetic Universal on providing me with coffee and biscuits. You needn't have bothered to sweeten the pill. I didn't really expect you to offer me any help or even encouragement. I regarded you as a hard-headed, inflexible, totally ruthless business tycoon from the moment we met.'

With narrowed eyes he rasped, 'So it must give you immense satisfaction to know that your first impressions of me were correct. It might also help you a little in facing up to the unfortunate fact that you've failed in your mission.'

She was glad he could not see the tears behind her eyes, or feel the desperate dryness of her mouth. 'I never expected to succeed. The person I'm most sorry for is my mother. She's the one who urged me to come. She—she had great faith in your—your integrity, whereas I had none.'

His jaw hardened. 'I resent that. My *integrity* was never in question. It was my—and my company's—generosity you tested. It just didn't come off, did it?' He moved. 'Let me show you to the door.'

So he was dismissing her! He opened the door and as she went through, he said, his eyes sweeping over her drooping figure, 'You should have laughed, Miss

Baird. Don't you recall what I said at the start of our interview? If you laughed more you could wring a man's last penny from him. But you didn't even smile.'

He closed the door on her. Only then, as she walked away down the corridor, did Lisette let her lips tremble and her eyes cloud with tears.

CHAPTER FIVE

LISETTE arrived home to find the house empty. She was glad she did not have to face her mother's disappointment yet. She had not even had the energy to return to her office at the factory.

When she had telephoned Bob from a callbox at the station, he had taken the news with his usual equanimity. 'We'll just have to think of something else,' he had said.

Lying on her bed, Lisette stared at the ceiling and thought about the calamity that faced them. Finding no answer, she did not give up. She sought yet again for a solution. Yes, that was it, something would have to be sacrificed. She considered their personal assets— clothes, her mother's jewellery, the car which was used only occasionally when her mother visited friends in another town. That was the first thing that would have to go. But it would not solve all the problems.

Money was their need, a large sum of money ... Lisette sat up. The house! A great amount of capital was tied up in the place they lived in. The price of the house had been high even when her father had bought it. Since then its value must surely have increased.

But—she lay back—it was their home, the possession her mother most prized. It was in the exclusive area in which, she had told her husband, she had always wanted to live. The house, when they had viewed it, had been desirable beyond her expectations. Why, she had said, none of her friends lived in such a beautiful residence as this! So it had been purchased out of the profits from the factory—at that time the business had been making a profit—and the family had moved there.

No, her mother would never agree to selling the house. It held so many memories of her husband, so many mementoes of the happy life they had spent together. The carpets, furniture and draperies had been bought to fit exactly. Alterations had been made, a second bathroom added, the kitchen entirely re-equipped, the garden landscaped.

Lisette closed her eyes and a hopeless kind of sleep overtook her. Her interview with the head of Emu products had exhausted her. She awoke to find her mother standing beside her bed.

'I just had to wake you, dear,' said Evelyn. 'I couldn't wait to hear the news.' Her eyes were bright, her hands clasped.

It pained Lisette to have to shatter her illusions, but the sooner the deed was accomplished, the better. She swung her feet to the floor.

'It failed, Mother.' She could not watch the disappointment which must have wiped the pleasurable anticipation clean away from her mother's face. 'Or perhaps I should say, I failed.'

'But—but why, dear?' Evelyn sounded bewildered. 'I didn't think—I couldn't see how he could refuse you anything.'

'Mother,' Lisette gave a weak smile, 'I didn't go as a friendly acquaintance. I went as a business woman. And —and that was how he saw me—minus the "business".' She drew a sharp breath and covered her face. 'As—as a woman, nothing else. All he did was—was insult me.'

'Oh, dear!' Evelyn sat beside her daughter and put an arm round her shoulders. 'Dear, dear me.' A long silence was broken by cars passing below, boys calling to each other, the ring of someone else's telephone coming through an open window.

'What does Bob say?' Evelyn asked at length. Lisette

88

removed her hands from her face and told her.

'I've been thinking and thinking, Mother, but I haven't got anywhere. We need money. We *must* get it from somewhere.'

'Stanley?' Evelyn ventured. 'Stanley Burlington?'

'Impossible. Not the large amount we need. Mother,' Lisette turned to her, 'are there any assets we have that I don't know about—savings, investments?'

'Not a thing left. We've gone through it all.' Evelyn stood and walked round her daughter's room. It was large, with a wash basin and vanity unit along one wall. There were built-in cupboards full of clothes, largely unworn. The carpet and curtains were of top quality materials, echoing the furnishings of the rest of the house. The bed was the best that money, at that time, could buy.

From the window, Evelyn looked down at the garden with its rockery and fish pool, its sundial and wooden bench; at the swimming pool installed at the end of the garden. Leslie Baird had spared no expense to please his wife.

'Lisette,' Evelyn addressed her daughter in a small, breathless voice, 'there's the house.'

With grateful eyes, which filled as she acknowledged the extent of the sacrifice her mother was suggesting, Lisette looked at her. 'I hoped you would say that, Mother,' she said with infinite compassion. 'It's the only way.'

The estate agent valued the house at an even higher figure than Lisette had anticipated. With Bob Farrell's help, she started at once to apportion the money the agent had said they could expect to receive from a buyer for the property.

Part of the money, of course, would have to go towards a smaller dwelling for Lisette and her mother. Evelyn thought a flat—a modern, luxury flat would suffice. Lisette advised her to stop thinking in terms of 'luxury'.

'We'll probably end up living in two or three rooms,' she warned. 'Our standards will have to drop considerably. You do realise that, don't you, Mother?'

Mrs Baird frowned, not liking the idea at all, but accepting the fact at last, saying she would make any sacrifice to save the family firm. But when Lisette had told her that many of their possessions would have to go because there simply would not be room for them in a flat, Evelyn had almost cried.

From then on, she went around the house saying, 'Whatever we do, we can't part with this,' and 'Come what may, we must keep that.' Lisette shook her head behind her mother's back, telling herself that by the time they came to move out, her mother would have become reconciled.

As yet, they had told only Bob, no one else. He was a frequent visitor to the house and even went round with Lisette looking at possible places in which she and her mother might live.

About a month after Lisette's disastrous inteview with Rosco Hamden, Evelyn said, 'I phoned Bette Burlington this morning, dear, and asked her and Stanley over for the evening.' When her daughter did not comment, she went on, 'They're coming. I thought it would make a nice change to have company.'

Lisette nodded and managed a smile, and her mother was satisfied by the response.

The Burlingtons ... In her mind Lisette inevitably associated them with Rosco Hamden. She had not forgotten him. He remained with her day and night, in her dreams and in her thoughts. Now and then she found her hand wandering to the telephone. If only she could hear his voice ...

Then she would remember how difficult it had been that other time she had tried to contact him, how she had had to overcome the obstacles of telephonist and secretary, not to mention the appointments diary. Quickly she would draw her hand from the telephone and clench it in her lap. She would never forget his cold dismissal of her plea for help, and of herself from his room. Even now, she coloured deeply at the humiliation of being shown the door.

'You can ask Bob, too, dear,' Evelyn was saying. 'He'll be company for you, won't he? He's such a pleasant young man. And clever, too. He can discuss ——' she checked herself, eyeing her daughter warily, 'he can talk to Stanley about—well, about almost anything, can't he?'

Lisette let her mother think she had been fooled, but as she turned away she smiled to herself. No doubt her mother thought that, where her daughter had failed to obtain help for the firm, Bob might succeed. After all, Stanley Burlington held an important position as secretary of the local Chamber of Trade, and was a respected citizen of the town. Naturally, he had business contacts ...

Evelyn had prepared savouries and brought from the cupboard their two or three bottles of drink. She arranged the best tea service on a tray and put it all on the elaborately designed trolley which she wheeled into the living-room. Lisette helped her mother to arrange the savouries on dishes, then they both went upstairs to dress.

Although it was only Bob Farrell who was coming to keep her company, Lisette decided to choose one of her more attractive dresses. It would please her mother if she took some care with her appearance.

It was a Saturday and earlier in the day she had washed her hair. Now it hung softly to frame her face and curl gently round her small ears. The off-centre parting added a piquancy to her looks which arrested the eye of even a casual onlooker.

She made herself smile at her own reflection, wondering what it was about it that had made Rosco Hamden urge her to smile more often. All she could see was a set of white teeth inside lips which, she thought, might just be called 'inviting'. But she certainly could not see anything special about it. She shrugged. There was no accounting for other people's tastes.

The dress she wore was bright yellow crêpe. In style it was well-fitting and sleeveless. The neckline was low-cut, shaping to narrow bands passing over her shoulders. The white beads she hung round her neck matched the pendant earrings which swung from her ears. Her mother could not fault her appearance even if she tried.

Bob was the first to arrive. He bent to put his lips to Lisette's, but he did not touch her otherwise. Lisette thought, He's as passionless as I am. If a niggling doubt crept into her mind, she dismissed it. What did it matter? They were not even engaged. Lisette wondered if he had any feeling for her at all.

He lowered his tall, thin frame beside Mrs Baird on the long settee. As he talked to her, he hugged one knee in a boyish, slightly gauche way. Despite his age, which was nearly twenty-seven, he was nervous and awkward in company, but Lisette knew this did not reflect on his mental ability. He was intelligent and quick to learn. Moreover, he possessed something that endeared him to Evelyn Baird's heart—concern for the well-being and survival of the family business.

'I'll get the coffee going,' said Lisette, after rearranging a display of flowers which stood on a bookcase near the french windows.

'Let me help,' Bob said, starting up.

Lisette began to shake her head, but her mother said, 'A good idea, Bob. You can make sure she puts coffee in the percolator and not tea. She's absent-minded lately, that daughter of mine. She must be in love!'

Lisette coloured and swept out. Her mother's humour was too near the truth for comfort. She heard Bob say, 'I expect she's preoccupied with the factory. It's probably weighing on her mind.'

'Isn't it on all of our minds!' was Evelyn's prompt response.

As Lisette put the finishing touches to the food and heated water for the coffee, she and Bob talked books. It was her only escape, apart from music, from the cares which darkened most of her waking hours. He loved books as much as she did, and when away from the factory, they spent much of their time together discussing the latest books they had read.

Lisette looked at the cups and saucers on the tray and frowned. 'My mother can't count. She's put out too many.'

Lisette stood in the kitchen doorway and called along the hall, 'Mother!'

The door chimes rang and Evelyn hurried to welcome her guests. She seemed so eager, Lisette was puzzled. Her mother saw Bette Burlington on average every other day.

Bob was in the kitchen just behind Lisette and, with his hands hanging loosely beside him, watched the guests enter.

Bette Burlington came in first, her summer-weight coat swinging from her shoulders, her face radiant. She greeted Evelyn as though they had not met for years. Stanley followed, stepping over the threshold and giving Evelyn a bear hug. A man appeared behind them, pocketing keys as though he had just locked a car.

Lisette felt herself sway. Bob, behind her, must have noticed. His large hands came up to rest on her shoulders, steadying her. So her mother had known that Rosco would be accompanying the Burlingtons but had not told her, probably because she might make a scene!

She stared into two painfully familiar grey eyes, topped by thick, dark brows and even thicker hair. The faint, irritating smile, as it rested on the tableau made by the girl with the boy-friend protecting and possessively claiming her—or so it seemed—held a twist of cynicism. But when the smile was turned on Evelyn, it changed magically into charm and warmth. His manner, as he told Lisette's mother how pleased he was that they were meeting again, was relaxed and easy. This was, after all, a social occasion.

Lisette, still stunned, walked away from Bob's hands and greeted the newcomers. Bette kissed her on the cheek and Stanley gave her the same kind of bear hug he had given her mother. When it came to Rosco, she lifted to him an unsmiling face and introduced Bob Farrell. They shook hands and Bob followed the others into the living-room.

'Good evening, Mr Hamden,' said Lisette, and turned to go with Bob.

'Miss Baird.' Rosco's voice detained her. His hand came out. He was a guest. She could not ignore it.

Her hand rested in his, but as she started to pull hers away, he retained it by tightening his grip.

'A touching domestic scene in the kitchen doorway,' he said. 'The *understanding* boy-friend, I take it?'

'Bob works with me,' she said shortly, still trying to disengage her hand. 'I told you, he's a *friend*. Now will you let me join the others?' Another tug—in vain. He watched her efforts to free herself, then smiled.

'You can't get away from me fast enough, can you?'

'What do you expect? I haven't forgotten the way you practically threw me out of your room at your place of work, the way you cast me from your august presence,' she said acidly.

His lips curved, his eyes gleamed like sun on frozen water. 'You think I was a bit hard on you?'

'When you visited me at *my* place of work, I treated you politely, showed you round——'

'Ah, but I didn't come to beg, borrow or steal as you did when you visited me.'

'Steal?'

He released her hand at last and she tried to rub away the stiffness he had created in her fingers. 'Yes, steal. That's what it would have been if you had taken my company's money to prop up your failing business. I'd have seen the last of that money. You would never have been in a position to repay it. It would have gone nowhere, would it, the amount I would have been empowered by my Board of Directors to lend you. To make your factory viable again you'd need thousands of pounds poured into it, not an insignificant loan.'

'Well,' she responded defiantly, 'you can do that,' she snapped her fingers, 'with your loan! We don't need it now.'

The door of the living-room had swung shut and Lisette turned to push it, but Rosco stopped her and turned her roughly.

'What the hell do you mean, don't need it now? What have you done so that you can manage to carry on the business without an injection of money?'

Her stormy eyes met his. 'Sold my soul, Mr Hamden, that's what I've done, and now I'm damned for the rest of my life. Will you let me go?' She tried to twist away.

'You'll explain that, young woman, or I'll put you across my knee!'

'Lisette, Rosco!' Evelyn's voice drifted out. 'Come on in, you two. We can all hear you're quarrelling with each other!'

Rosco's anger abated, but only by a few degrees. Lisette flung a triumphant look at him and went into

95

the living-room, leaving the door open for her guest to enter on his own. She knew it was rude, but she was past caring.

Stanley made room for Lisette on the settee and Bob rose deferentially, offering Rosco his seat. Rosco waved him down again and placed himself astride a velvet upholstered footstool near to Bob. It was not long before the two men were deep in conversation. As Bob spoke, Rosco listened intently, eyes down, seeing nothing, his attention completely absorbed by what Bob Farrell was saying.

'Well,' said Stanley, playfully putting his arm round Lisette, 'how's my favourite girl?' Lisette turned to smile at him and he said, 'My word, you dazzle a man when you do that, Lisette. Bette,' his wife turned, 'watch out, this dark-haired witch is bewitching me!'

They laughed, but the laughter was not general. The other two men appeared not to have heard. Their conversation continued uninterrupted. Stanley, having asked permission, dispensed the drinks and still Rosco and Bob talked.

Lisette began to feel stirrings, not so much of jealousy as of anger, that Rosco Hamden should talk so seriously to Bob—it was the business they were discussing, that much was plain—yet be so condescending and prejudiced whenever she approached him on business matters.

A new resentment began to stir. Bob had come to keep her company, yet here he was, ignoring her completely. Thanks to Rosco Hamden's unexpected presence, *she* was the odd one out.

She grew so restless she said, 'I'll go and see to the food, Mother.'

Evelyn nodded, pausing in her conversation with Bette and Stanley. 'Thanks, dear,' she said absently, and went on talking.

The two younger men did not even notice that she

went from the room and Lisette's spirits drooped. If the whole evening was going on like this, she might as well go up to her bedroom. She uncovered the food and saw to the coffee. When it was almost ready, she became conscious of being watched. Swiftly she turned and saw Rosco in the doorway, hands in pockets.

He was smiling, but it was a smile she mistrusted because it contained no mockery. And Rosco Hamden never smiled at her with sincerity, so what was on his mind?

'Why did you come this evening?' she challenged, aware of her rudeness to a guest, but uncaring of it. Was she ever polite to this man? she wondered agitatedly. But he had given her so much pain, wasn't it time she inflicted some on him?

He was as unhurt as if she had thrust at him with a stage-prop dagger. His smile broadened. 'First, I was invited here, being at the moment a guest of the Burlingtons. Second, or should I say first?—I came to see you. Our last meeting ended so—unsatisfactorily.'

She turned from him to wash a saucepan. 'That was your fault. You showed me the door—literally.'

'You had just insulted my integrity. What else did you expect?'

'So I hurt your pride? Now who's reducing everything to personal terms as you accuse me of doing?'

'I said integrity. You said pride,' he reminded her quietly.

Lisette was silent, continuing to wash the saucepan.

'So you don't want a loan now? Since I know damned well you haven't, as you put it so melodramatically, "sold your soul", what exactly have you done?'

She paused in her work. 'Put the house up for sale.'

'You've *what*?'

He seemed so angry she stopped washing the saucepan and dried her hands.

'Whose idea was that?' he demanded. 'Yours, I suppose? How can you be so unfeeling as to deprive your mother of the house she obviously loves——?'

'It was her idea! I—I thought of it but didn't dare suggest it. She thought of it, too, and I agreed.' She put her back against the sink. 'What else is there for us to do?' she cried. 'There's no other way of getting the money we need. Anyway, my father bought the house out of the firm's profits, like a lot of other things. So we'll merely be returning the money where it really belongs, won't we?'

'But you've got to live somewhere.'

Lisette shrugged. 'We'll rent a flat or a couple of rooms.'

'And the furniture, all your possessions?'

She stared down at the black and white floor tiles. 'Sell them, I suppose. Get as much as we can for them.'

'You know the money you'll get for the property will be peanuts compared with the vast injection of funds you really need to bring the firm back on its feet?' Lisette did not answer. 'Had many offers for the place?'

Reluctantly she answered, 'None. It's at the higher end of the property market and the estate agent said there are few buyers at present in this price range.'

'So the gamble hasn't paid off?'

'There's plenty of time,' she lied.

'Is there?' She moved to stare out at the dying early summer evening. She heard him move and stiffened. 'I know differently, Lisette. I've been talking to your boyfriend.'

Two hands came to rest on her shoulders as Bob's had done earlier, but these hands gripped and sent shivers up and down her body. The touch of these hands made her want to tremble, to lie against his solidity, feel the security of his arms around her ...

As if reading her thoughts—perhaps she had given herself away somehow—he pulled her backwards and she felt his lean, hard body pressed against hers. Those hands ran over her shoulders and down to her wrists, shifted, finding her hips and insinuating their way up, up, meeting the curve of her breasts and lingering momentarily. Then they turned her quickly and she found herself in his arms. It was not security she felt, as she had imagined—it was a dangerous, burning excitement which, as his lips found hers and, this time, prised them apart, a throbbing awareness of the needs of her own body.

His hand cupped the back of her head, his other curled round her, gaining an intimate hold on her. He moulded her to him and she was powerless under his stroking caresses, the expertise of his lovemaking. She could not even cry out to him to stop because his lips were fastened so firmly over hers.

Voices drifted in from the living-room, bringing them back to the present. Rosco released her slightly and held her away, gazing into her eyes in the darkening kitchen, and searching—for capitulation? For an acknowledgment of his power over her, his ability to turn her into a yearning, supplicating woman?

'Bob's in there,' she gasped. 'He'll—he'll——'

'Will he?' A mocking smile, bright, baiting eyes coloured his words. 'He's a *very* understanding young man, isn't he? I have your mother's word for it. And I've spent some time talking to him. I've discovered how intelligent he is.'

'I suppose,' she fought to free herself, 'if *he* had come and asked you for financial help, you would have given it. But because *I* came, you refused.'

'You could be right,' he murmured, contemplating the curve of her lips, 'you could be right, Miss Baird.'

'Please let me go.'

'In a moment, after the second kiss I intend to take. The other was so satisfactory I fancy another.' He closed the gap between them, bringing his lips down on hers again.

'Oh—oh, sorry.' An apologetic voice came from the doorway. They pulled apart and Lisette, flushed and guilty, looked at Bob. Rosco slipped his hands into his pockets and watched.

Bob looked from one to the other. 'I—I just came to see how you were getting on with the coffee.' He withdrew and returned to the living-room.

'Good God,' Rosco murmured, 'some boy-friend! He should have knocked me to the floor. If I'd caught another man kissing my woman, I'd have done so. I would have had no compunction.'

'No,' Lisette responded, smoothing her hair and grabbing at the remains of her pride, 'you haven't, have you—any compunction? I mean in *anything*. You're hard as granite.'

'I'm an industrialist,' he said blandly, 'one of those "captains of industry" the country can't do without. In all but certain circumstances, such as the one that has just come to an end between us, hardness and inflexibility are in my guts.'

'You're impossible!' she snapped.

He grinned and took the tray of crockery from her. 'That's better than being obnoxious, as you called me not so long ago.'

For the rest of the evening Lisette avoided Rosco Hamden. Whenever he came near, she moved away. She did her best to stay at Bob's side, although he showed a marked reluctance to get too near her.

He strayed towards some bookshelves which occupied a corner of the room. Lisette followed and whispered, 'Bob, I'm sorry about—about what you saw. It wasn't my fault. He—he forced himself on me.' Which, she soothed her conscience, was the partial truth. She did not add that she had done little to get herself out of the situation.

He said in a strained tone, 'All right, I understand. I suppose there's not much a girl can do in those circumstances.' With a weak smile, 'After all, we are doing our best to enlist his help, aren't we?'

So, Lisette thought, dismayed, he assumed that she had tolerated Rosco's kiss for the sake of the firm? Did he really think her morals were as questionable as that?

She felt Rosco's eyes on them and saw his cynical smile. Soon afterwards, Evelyn's guests departed. Lisette went with her mother into the hall to see them off. Bob remained in the living-room.

As Rosco left, following the Burlingtons out, he whispered to Lisette, 'Has he forgiven you, or have I broken up a beautiful friendship?'

Evelyn went outside to see her guests into the car.

'I told you,' Lisette whispered back furiously, 'there's nothing—well, tangible between us.' There was a burst of ribald laughter from Rosco. 'I mean,' she added irritably, 'I mean, no promises, no ring,' she held out her hand, 'no engagement.'

'Which leaves the field open for me.'

She shook her head violently. 'I'd shut the gate and padlock it against you!'

'You're a brazen hypocrite,' he jeered. 'After that kiss I gave you tonight and the way you responded, I could make you give me anything I wanted.'

Her eyes blazed into his. 'Just you try, Mr Hamden, just you try!'

He smiled lazily. 'I will some time, lady, I certainly will.' He lifted his hand in a mocking salute and disappeared into the darkness.

'Last night,' Bob said next morning, 'Mr Hamden said we've got two choices. Either we find someone to take us over or we go bankrupt.'

At her desk, Lisette ran her finger over the dust which clung to the telephone.

'I asked him if he was interested in buying Baird Shoes, Lisette.' She looked up. 'But he said no. His company would never agree, he said, even if he asked them. And he made it clear he wouldn't be doing any asking. It seems we've gone too far downhill for that.'

Lisette looked at Bob resolutely. 'We'll have to hang on, Bob, until Mother and I find a buyer for the house. Two months now since we put it on the market and so far fewer than half a dozen people looking over it and not one offer.'

Two weeks passed and it was late June, two weeks since the night of the kiss, as Lisette had come to think of it. A fortnight since she had seen Rosco Hamden. The longing was in her to see him again, a longing which she knew would probably never be fulfilled. There was a whole lifetime in front of her in which to reconcile herself to the fact that she was deeply in love with a man she would almost certainly never see again. Anyway, what good would it do if she did? He looked upon her with the deepest contempt, didn't he?

That afternoon the telephone rang. Irritably, Lisette lifted the receiver. 'Baird Shoes,' she said wearily.

'Found a buyer for your house yet?' In the space of two seconds, the familiar voice had her heartbeats hammering.

'No,' she snapped, angry with herself for the delight she felt in hearing his voice again.

'Gone bankrupt yet?' he mocked.

'No!' she shouted.

'Found anyone to take you over yet?' A breathing pause. 'In the business sense, I mean,' he drawled, 'not you personally, naturally.'

She replied stiffly, 'I don't believe in takeovers, Mr Hamden, and you know it.'

'Ah, yes. You explained the day we met. It's not fair, I think you said, for giants like my company to keep pushing out the small family business. Let me think of the exact words. "Big is bad, small is beautiful." Isn't that right? "I don't believe in monopolies." Right

102

again? "My firm isn't for sale." Another quote? "Even if it were, I wouldn't let you buy it." Correct? Oh, and,' she almost heard him smile, 'the name's Rosco.'

The phone clicked in her ear. As Lisette replaced the receiver, she felt like crying.

Three days later, Bob Farrell came into her office. It was a Friday and Lisette felt tired with an 'end of the week' exhaustion.

'Trouble,' he said, and her heart dived even lower, which she had not thought possible. 'Big trouble, Lisette.'

'Go on,' she said, clenching her teeth. 'I can take it—just.'

'While you were busy phoning round for orders this morning, I had a visit from a member of the local Trades Council.'

Lisette frowned. 'I've heard of them, but I'm not sure of their function.'

'Well, this council represents all the trades unions in the town. He said he was speaking on behalf of the employees of Baird Shoes. It's been brought to his notice, he said, that the workers at this factory are not only being paid less than the established union rates for the job, but were actually being paid less than the legal minimum.'

Lisette paled. This was worse than she had expected. 'So what does he want us to do about it?'

'Well, he said he wanted to assure me—and you, of course—that he'd had no complaints about management–worker relations at all. It seems the employees regard them as excellent.'

Bob gave a small smile of encouragement and Lisette tried to echo it.

'The representative said that, unfortunately, we had a reputation in the town as bad payers.'

'Didn't you tell him,' said Lisette, tensing as the mental load she bore grew still heavier, 'that when our fortunes are on the up-turn, we'll bring the rates of pay up to union levels?'

'I tried but got nowhere. He then requested officially that the management increase the wage rates not only to those required by law, but to the amount which the trade union in question had negotiated at national level.'

Lisette gripped the edge of the desk. 'Bob, we can't. We simply haven't the money available. Where's the extra finance going to come from?'

'You know what it means if we don't, Lisette?'

She stared at him as he sat on a corner of her desk. 'A strike?'

'What else?'

'But it would be the end of everything. Don't they understand? They'd lose their jobs because the jobs would simply cease to exist. The factory would have to close.'

'I agree. We're facing bankruptcy, Lisette.'

Evelyn Baird broke down when Lisette told her of the serious situation which faced them. Lisette tried to comfort her, but in the end she had had no choice but to let her mother cry herself dry.

Even then Lisette had not dared to tell her the whole truth. She felt she must leave her mother with some hope, just in case they found a solution, although in her heart, Lisette acknowledged that this was very unlikely indeed.

Evelyn stared into space, crumpled handkerchief in her hand. 'Suppose,' she said, 'suppose *I* approach Rosco for a loan. Do you think he would help if I asked him as a special favour?' Lisette suppressed a smile at her mother's naïvety where the savage jungle of the business world was concerned. 'After all,' Evelyn persisted, 'I'm entitled to, aren't I, as part-owner with you.'

'Mother,' Lisette said gently, 'Rosco is adamant. Nothing will move him, nothing.'

Evelyn looked at her daughter appealingly. 'One more try, dear?' she whispered. 'Won't you make one more try? Think of it as not for yourself, or for the business, if you like, but—for me?'

Lisette walked about the room, not knowing whether to laugh or cry at her mother's self-centred attitude. Of course she loved her mother, but she could not reconcile herself to the way her mother assumed she was willing to sacrifice everything—yes, everything—for that love. Didn't she place any value on her daughter's dignity, self-respect and high ideals?

Something came over her—a fierce resentment she could not quell, a left-over pain from those overheard words between her parents so long ago. Lisette swung round.

'Do you want me to *offer myself* in exchange for the assurance of the continuance of Baird Shoes? Suppose I'd been the son you both wanted? You couldn't have asked him to grovel, could you? And if I go and see Rosco Hamden again and plead for his help, I'd be grovelling, make no mistake about it.'

Her mother did not reprimand her as she had the last time she had been so outspoken. The end was in sight now. Then, it had been no more than a possibility, a spectre haunting them—and as everyone knew, Evelyn had probably reasoned, ghosts don't really exist, do they? So the firm would carry on regardless, something, someone would save it and they would be able to keep their privileged way of life, their high standard of living.

'We—we wouldn't have to sell the house, Lisette, if he lent us the money instead,' Evelyn whispered, the dullness in her eyes being replaced by a prodding encouragement.

Lisette rounded on her mother. 'So you want me to—

to *debase* myself, because that's what it would be, to save the firm—*and* the roof over our heads?'

Evelyn was silent. It was that silence, that failure to refute the statement, to deny that that was what she had meant, that reduced Lisette to the depths of despair.

Through the night, Lisette tossed and turned. In the morning she awoke, heavy-eyed, sick at heart. She knew what she had to do.

CHAPTER SIX

LISETTE obtained Rosco Hamden's private address from Stanley Burlington. When she had contacted him, Stanley had asked,

'Why do you want to see him, dear? Or,' with a meaningful pause, 'is that a rude question?'

'It's a—a personal matter, Mr Burlington.'

'Ah, I see.' He had laughed and rung off.

So easy, so much the established thing these days, the selling by a woman of her attractions to get what she wanted from a man. Stanley had accepted at once the reason why—or so he had thought—she wanted to visit Rosco Hamden. He had probably not guessed that she had wanted anything from Rosco, having assumed instead that they were indulging in a secret love affair.

Or, in asking for his private address, that she, Lisette, had it in mind to start one. It was common practice in these liberated days, wasn't it, for the suggestion to come from the woman? Let's make love, let's go to bed, let's have an affair. I'll live with you until I find—or you find—someone else?

On the way there, she had to persuade herself that she was no different from other young women of today. Deep down the idea revolted her, but the persuasion was vital in order to give herself courage. *Like a lamb to the slaughter*. The phrase kept repeating. But the 'slaughter' would be lovemaking—and would Rosco's lovemaking be so bad?

It would be good, it would be a joy—to her. To him it would be mechanical, automatic, a reflex action by his male responses to a willing, even eager woman. He would give of his lovemaking freely, not because of any feeling he would have for her—Lisette knew he had none—but because it would give him pleasure as a man.

Afterwards—what was 'afterwards' like? She simply did not know and she shrank from the self-disgust she would feel, the derisive smile he would give her when the passion had died. Afterwards she would whisper, Please, Rosco, help me get the family business on its feet. And, so the rumour went, he would give her everything she asked for.

The train was nearing the terminus and she panicked. She would get the next train home. She couldn't go through with it ... An image came to her of her mother crying, the crumpled face, the hopeless look in those helpless eyes—and Lisette went on along the platform to where the ticket collector stood.

The Underground train took her inexorably to Epping, a country area within easy reach of London where Rosco Hamden lived. It was in a block of luxury flats, Stanley had explained. He lived there for convenience. He had a house in the West Country to which he went for occasional breaks and longer holidays.

There it was, a six-storey block of luxury apartments. Third floor, Stanley had said. There was a lift, but Lisette chose to walk. It would take longer that way. Along a corridor and there, over a bell outside the door, was a label bearing the inscription, Rosco Hamden. Her finger stretched towards the bell—and stopped. What would she say? How could she explain her appearance on his doorstep on a Saturday afternoon?

Could she talk to him? she would ask. It was urgent, otherwise she wouldn't have troubled him at the weekend. Yes, that was it, she would keep everything on a business level all the time. No personalities involved, no intimacies. When she told him the extent of her troubles—far worse now than the last time she had seen him—he would see reason.

Once, twice, she pressed the bell. No reply, no sound —maybe he was out? Oh, the relief if he were! Gone to his house in the West Country, perhaps?

The door opened. A woman stood there, hand on hip, insolence and irritation in her eyes. She was long-haired, blonde and beautiful, dressed from head to foot in a scarlet cat-suit, her waist encircled by a gilt belt, while gold bangles hung from her wrists.

'What do you want?' Her eyes as well as her voice, dismissed Lisette as a nonentity.

'I'm sorry.' Lisette half-turned. 'I must have come to the wrong flat. I thought Mr Hamden lived here. I——'

'He does. He's busy. He doesn't see callers on a Saturday.'

One of his women? Lisette thought dully. Which of his 'moods' did this woman suit? No need to wonder, really. One look at the hidden 'tigress' in her was enough to tell the most naïve of persons. And had she, Lisette Baird, thought she could arouse the man to a strength of feeling sufficient to desire *her*, make love to *her* and afterwards ...

'I'm sorry to have disturbed you,' said Lisette, turning away.

'A girl,' she heard the woman say over her shoulder. 'Don't bother yourself, Rosco. She's not worth the effort. God, you could find better than that in the top class of a girls' school!'

Lisette quickened her footsteps along the corridor.

'Lisette!'

She began to run.

'*Lisette!*' There was a command in the call she could not ignore. Her footsteps slowed to a stop. She turned, breathing heavily. 'Will you come back, please!'

It was not a question. From the tone, she would disobey at her peril. With something like fear, she retraced her steps. As she reached his door, she saw that the woman had gone inside. Rosco stood outside.

'Did you want to see me?' His tone was neutral, which helped just a little.

'Well, yes, but—you're busy. It can wait.'

'I'm not *busy*. And if you've taken the trouble to come all the way here from where you live, it can't wait. Come on in.'

He grasped her wrist and pulled her in, slamming the door with his foot. 'Wanda!' he called.

The woman emerged from a door which opened wide to reveal a bed. It had been made. It was not rumpled. But it was a bed.

Rosco motioned to the entrance door with his head. 'You'd better go.' As an afterthought, 'Please.'

The woman called Wanda went across to him, hips moving from side to side. 'But darling, you promised, today——' Her hands rested against his chest. He released Lisette's wrist and gripped the woman's wrists, jerking them from him.

'I made no promises. I never do. I'd be glad if you would leave. I have a visitor.'

'But darling,' Wanda pouted, 'I'm a visitor, too.' It was plain from her tone that she knew he meant what he said. She had to go.

She went back into the bedroom, collected a coat and bag and paused at the door, giving Lisette a look of cool insolence. 'I can be sure of one thing, darling,' she murmured. 'Whatever she's come for, it's strictly business. With her to entertain, you couldn't possibly think of anything else.'

Moments later they were alone, and only then did Lisette become aware of the luxury in which Rosco Hamden lived. The living area spread wide into corners which were occupied by bookshelves, hi-fi equipment, stands with pot plants in full bloom.

The carpet's velvet-soft pile was a pale brown, matching the floor-length velvet curtains and the upholstery of the velvet-covered unit suite which stood in a curve in the centre of the room. One armless matching chair, taken from the unit, stood apart.

On a low, glass-topped table stood two glasses. Both had been used. An ashtray was half filled with cigarette stubs and the smell of smoke hung in the air. Since Rosco did not smoke, the smoker could only have been his lady friend. She had left part of herself behind. No doubt thoughts of her lingered in Rosco's mind, too. He probably cursed the disturbance of his day's relaxation with the woman who suited his weekend mood.

'Nice to see you, Lisette,' he said. It was the usual greeting of host to unexpected guest.

'I'm sorry I interrupted——'

'You interrupted nothing. Give me your coat.'

She slipped it from her shoulders and gave it to him. It was summerweight and midnight blue, matching the sleeveless dress which was finished at the neck and waist with touches of scarlet and white.

He looked her over. 'Neat, cool, remote. Like its wearer.' He took the coat into the bedroom and returned. 'Make yourself comfortable.' He motioned to the settee which had been formed by the placing together of the units. At each end there was a chair with one arm, thus forming the gently curving settee.

He went to a cabinet and opened the doors, taking out a bottle. He held it up, looking at her. She nodded. Yes, she thought, a drink would bolster her fast receding courage. She felt tense and awkward, as gauche almost as Bob Farrell in company. For a moment she longed for their easy relationship which asked nothing of her, and to which she contributed nothing.

Rosco came and stood before her, a glass in each hand. He smiled down at her and her heartbeats responded at once. Did he know how nervous she felt?

She reached out for a glass, but he drew it away.

'Say please.' So he had decided to tease. He sat beside her.

'Please,' she whispered, and took the glass from him. She swallowed some liquid too quickly and choked.

Back it came, that memory of the time they had first met, the mocking look in his eyes from the other side of the room as she had drunk and choked until her eyes ran.

'Good grief, it's not brandy!' he said, taking the glass and putting it down. His hand hit her back and she managed to stop, taking the handkerchief he had pushed into her palm.

'Sorry,' she muttered into its soft, sweet-smelling folds, and dabbed at her eyes. His hand remained on her back. She wished it would move, but checked the thought. Wasn't that the object of her visit—that she should not only tolerate his touch but encourage it?

The choking, and its aftermath, passed and she turned to smile at him. It was a watery smile, but its effect on him was electric. Their eyes held, the smile dissolved and a deep seriousness took its place. His hand lifted to her hair which he stroked a couple of times. She held herself taut, not wanting him to stop.

'Relax,' he urged softly. 'I won't eat you.'

She smiled again, tentatively. 'Not even for your mid-morning snack?'

He laughed, throwing back his head as if remembering the occasion on which he had used the phrase. 'I—might do other things with you, but not eat you. If I ate you, I wouldn't—have you, would I? You'd be gone.'

Her smile held and she nodded. Foolish talk, but what did it matter?

'Dare I ask,' he said, 'why you came?'

It took some courage to reply, but she managed it. 'To—to see you.'

'That's all? No qualifications, like "on business" or "I

was in the area so I called in case you were in"? Just "to see me"?'

This was easier than she had even dreamed. But he took his hand from her hair and rested his head against a cushion. His legs stretched in front of him, crossed at the ankles. His hands lifted to support his head. His brown shirt was short-sleeved and unfastened to the last button. The belt around his waist was of leather, his trousers a deep brown check. On his feet were leather sandals. It was the outfit of a man relaxing—with his woman—at home.

Lisette dragged her eyes away. Those strange, disturbing feelings were coming back to life. Even the sight of him now, she thought in dismay, was enough to ...

'How is your mother?' he asked into the silence.

She recalled her mother's tears, her pleas. 'Not—not very happy.'

'Oh, why?' She glanced at him and found that his eyes were closed.

Now was her chance. 'She's worried.' Having got this far, Lisette thought, I might as well plunge on. 'About the business.'

She might have spoken to a picture on the wall for all the response she received.

After a few moments he said, 'Let's forget business. At weekends I put it out of my mind.'

So, with a few words, he had dismissed the whole reason for her visit. He turned to her. 'You know something? You've given me a pleasant surprise. I thought you were the sort of girl who waited to be invited, who didn't dare put her nose inside a man's home unless she received a formal invitation, complete with R.S.V.P. in large letters.'

At once she stood up. 'I'm sorry, Mr Hamden. I didn't intend to intrude on your privacy.' Why did

113

she have to feel as immature and awkward as a thirteen-year-old?

He reached out and pulled her back beside him. 'I'm not criticising. I'm pleased you've come. And Lisette,' his hand against her cheek drew her face round, 'the name's Rosco.'

'I know.'

'So why don't you say it?' She pressed her lips together. 'Look, you came all this way to see me. I'm not sure why—yet—but I'm delighted to see *you*. So why don't you relax? Forget our quarrels. Forget the insults we've thrown at each other in the past. Forget everything except that you came and we're here together.'

'Forget—the girl who was here?'

'Wanda? You can put her out of your mind.'

Yes, Lisette thought, standing and wandering across the room, as easily as you'll put me out of your mind after—after you've made love to me and I've gone.

She was drawn to his bookshelves and inspected their contents as he had looked at hers in her office. There was little in the way of fiction here, except for the works of a handful of famous names. There were books on company law, on many aspects of industry and management, on commerce, economics and electronics and even, to Lisette's surprise, the Industrial Revolution in Britain in the nineteenth century.

Hands crept round her upper arms. She felt his breath disturbing her hair. 'Impressed, my librarian friend?'

'Very. But, the fiction apart, they're way above my head.'

'Some of them shouldn't be. As managing director—pardon me,' with a grin, '*worker*-director of your company, you should understand much of this.'

She stirred uncomfortably under his touch. Why didn't he take his hands away? They were caressing her now, moving up, down, stroking, resting, creating chaos in her mind. 'I—well, I suppose I don't take it all as seriously as you do.'

His fingers tightened a little. 'And you wonder why the business is going downhill?'

She turned, breaking free of his hold. 'How could my reading books like these alter the economic situation that's caused our problems? Anyway, I told you that even when I took over after my father died, things were already going wrong.'

'If you'd had the knowledge, if you had known how to re-organise and had made better use of the overdraft the bank had granted your father——'

'It was almost gone when I took the business over. I told you that, too.'

He cupped her face and gazed into her troubled eyes. 'Forgive me. I swore I wouldn't talk business. This is a special occasion, not to be spoilt by arguments about management, loans, business troubles. Instead, we should celebrate. Lisette Baird, the hitherto untouchable, cool young woman, always very much on her dignity, has, of her own accord, come to see me. Let's toast the occasion in champagne.'

She smiled tremulously. 'I'd rather have a cup of tea.'

He burst out laughing, then placed a swift kiss on her mouth. 'I've caught that smile of yours with my lips. Next best to catching it with the camera.' He took her hand, seeming suddenly happy, younger, and to Lisette's still tortured thoughts—there was a kind of mountain to be climbed before she left him—unbelievably human and approachable.

'I offer her champagne,' he said, 'and she asks for tea! You shall have your tea, my sweet. You can indulge your proletarian tastes to your heart's content.'

He drew her behind him into his kitchen. It was equipped from floor to ceiling with cupboards, electrical equipment, all the appliances a housewife might dream about. 'All this and service, too. If I want a meal sent up, I dial and it's delivered.'

'Don't you ever cook for yourself?' she asked, aghast that so much luxury equipment should stand there unused.

'Only when I want a snack instead of a meal. Are you hungry? If you are, help yourself.' He opened store cupboards stocked with tins and packets, an upright freezer filled to capacity. 'Pretend you're a sweet little housewife instead of a formidable worker-director. Feed us both. Pretend you—belong here.'

She looked at him and caught his sardonic smile. Was it a trap? She would not fall into it. She shook her head. 'I'd be as out of place here,' she lied, 'as you would be working in my office at Baird Shoes.'

Did she imagine the veiled antagonism? It was gone in a moment, whatever it had been.

They drank the tea from bone china cups. Lisette collected the dishes and took them into the kitchen. Rosco did not attempt to stop her. He sat forward in his chair and watched. Nor did he offer to carry the tray, not that it was heavy. He was behaving like a husband after a few years of marriage. Was *he* playing the game of pretending she 'belonged'?

As the warm water ran into the bowl, he stood by the kitchen door and watched her wash the cups. What was his motive? Was he testing her? If so, to what end? He even watched her dry them. When she looked around for a place to put them, he said at last,

'Leave that for me.' He approached slowly, taking the tea towel from her and throwing it over a rail. 'You astonish me. You're the first woman who's been here who has done what you've just done. I was fascinated by the sight.' He was laughing at her, but she didn't mind.

'So I fit in with at least *one* of your moods? The domesticated, husband-like one, perhaps?'

'Husband?' He seized her in his arms and swung her round so that her face was towards the daylight. 'What are you after, wench—a wedding ring? That makes a change in itself. Most of your sex want jewellery, clothes, perfume.'

'A wedding ring is jewellery, isn't it?' she fenced. 'So that makes me no different from the others, does it?'

His hand moved down and he pressed her hips against his while her head hung back. 'A wedding ring is more than jewellery, and you know it, wench,' he baited. 'It carries with it promises, life-long devotion, kids—ties, unswerving faithfulness, goodbye to freedom.'

His words were hurting her so much he might have been twisting her arm. She told herself she was a fool, that woman to this man could never mean more than one thing—a tool for the appeasement of his sexual desire. He needed no wife, no beloved companion, no mother of his children—hadn't he just dismissed them as 'ties'?

She struggled to escape, but he would not let her. With all her strength she fought with him, but he won in the end by the simple trick of grasping her hair. If she moved, she hurt herself. If she stayed still, he hurt her. He had won.

He seemed invigorated by the struggle. He laughed, his face alive with the pleasure of winning. Then she was crushed in his arms and his mouth hit hers. No longer the gentle kisses of the past, but savagely demanding, enjoying the sweet taste of her mouth.

A change took place in her as his energy, his vigour and his demands began to seep into her. It was like an intravenous drip into a patient's bloodstream, flowing through her veins and filling her with quivering life and a heady excitement.

Rosco drew away, his eyes dazzling in their brightness. 'Why did you come, minx?' Lisette shook her head. She could not speak if she tried. 'Was it for this——' he kissed her lightly, 'and this?' Another swift kiss. She nodded. 'Did you like that other kiss I gave you in your home so much you wanted more?' She nodded again in a silent lie. That was not why she had come and soon he would know it. Her courage nearly left her, then she remembered her mother's pleading eyes.

'What about your boy-friend?' he said softly. 'Wouldn't he object?'

'He doesn't matter,' she whispered.

'That, my sweet, is all I wanted to know.' He swept her into his arms and into the living-room, placing her on the settee. He looked down at her. 'No,' he murmured, 'I can think of a better place.' He scooped her up and carried her through a door—the one through which the girl called Wanda had passed. It was his bedroom.

He dropped her on to the bed and threw himself beside her, pulling her round on to her side to face him. He found the zip fastener at the front of her dress and eased it down. His mouth touched her neck, her shoulders, the cleft between her breasts.

He moved until he was half over her and his lips parted hers forcibly, their teeth meeting in his ardour. His shirt had worked free of his slacks and his bare chest was like granite against her softness.

'Respond,' he urged, 'respond, sweetheart.'

But she couldn't, she could not let herself be swept along by the tide of his desire.

His kisses moved over her throat, her bared shoulders, and she cried out at the ecstasy that was the pain of his caresses.

When his lips found her breast, that was the moment her desire sprang to life and she pressed him to her, abandoning at last her restraint. For the first time in her life she was experiencing a man's lovemaking; for the first time in her life she had to acknowledge that she was no longer in control of her emotions.

He laughed in triumph at having aroused her to respond. 'There'll be no stopping me now, sweetheart,' he murmured, and his hand moved down to her waist, her hips ...

She stiffened and cried out, 'No!'

She felt the hammer of his heartbeat as his chest crushed hers, felt the roughness of the dark hair rub against her bare skin.

'You're resisting me,' he murmured, smiling into her eyes. 'I know a woman's tricks.'

'You don't know mine!'

The anguish in her voice must have reached him. All his movements were stilled. But his heart kept drumming, the desire she had excited in him did not quickly subside. He lay for some time, as if loath to move from her, to accept what she was trying to tell him.

She wanted him now as much as he wanted her. But she could not let him continue to the ultimate end under false pretences. Her conscience, her inherent honesty which, for her mother's sake, she had tried for once to disregard, would not allow her to surrender herself entirely to his demands without telling him the truth, however unbearable the pain of confessing her motives might be.

'I'm sorry,' she whispered.

At last he moved away and lay on his back. She hugged herself. Where his hands had held her so intimately, the flesh still ached from the pressure of his touch.

'My God, *you're* sorry!' Dragging out the words, he said, 'You're still a virgin. Is that true?'

Her hands spread over her face, her breath came in gasps.

Now, like a storm threatening from a distance, his anger began to gather. 'It was all a blind, wasn't it?

You're raw. You're totally inexperienced. So why did you choose me to break you in?'

She supposed she deserved the lash of his tongue. 'I'm s-sorry if I disappointed you. I d-didn't know you only made love to experienced women.'

'I've never met any other kind,' he said sarcastically. 'I didn't know any other sort existed these days.' He rested on his elbow, looking her over indolently. 'In the circumstances, don't you think you'd better draw on the small store of modesty I've left untouched in you and make yourself decent? Luckily for you—and the boy-friend who "doesn't matter"—I can exercise control over my reflexes even under the most extreme circumstances, although most men in my position in life would have taken immense delight in finishing what they had started.'

Lisette sat up and with trembling fingers searched for the tab of the zip fastener. Rosco reached out lazily, pushed her shaking hands away and did the job for her. He rested on his elbow again and, with amusement, watched her every movement, making her tingle. Then she lay back as if exhausted from an illness.

He did not bother to pull on his shirt which he had torn off, or fasten the belt around his waist which he had undone. 'Now tell me why you came.' He spoke abruptly, startling her. In the dark mood into which he had, without warning, plunged, she shrank from telling him.

Instead she said unsteadily, 'I'm sorry my coming made you send your girl-friend away. I'm sorry, too, for depriving you of your afternoon's pleasure.' She knew she was only postponing the moment of truth.

He knew it, too. 'Cut out the humbug. Tell me what I want to know.'

Her head flopped sideways on the pillow, away from him. How could she get the words out of her stiff lips? 'It was—I wanted ...' She tried again. 'I just hoped that—afterwards you'd—you would help——' She turned agonised eyes towards him as he still reclined, looking down at her. 'Don't you *understand*?'

'No, I don't.' It was impossible to tell whether he spoke the truth. His eyes were hooded and cool.

What she did comprehend was that he was having no mercy on her. He was making her tell him with her own lips. Nothing less appeared to satisfy him.

She closed her eyes. Her hair was strewn over the pillow on which her head rested. Her hands bunched into fists, clutching the bed cover, her bare toes curled and uncurled.

'Things have got much worse at the factory,' she began. He listened impassively. 'We need help badly, so badly that if we don't get it, we could be in trouble—real trouble.'

'Well?'

This was terrible. It was worse, far worse than she had envisaged. Haltingly she told him about the visit from the Trades' Council representative, how he had said that Bairds were paying below the legal minimum, let alone below union rates, and how they would have a strike on their hands if they failed to raise their rates of pay.

'Which,' he said, 'in view of your lack of funds, would mean closure?'

She nodded. 'Followed by bankruptcy.'

'And what did you think you'd gain by this?' He gestured first to her, then to himself, indicating what had so recently taken place between them.

Her sigh came from her depths and she shook her head, compressing her lips to stop their trembling.

'So,' he persisted mercilessly, removing himself from the bed and pulling on his shirt, 'you decided that the only way was to sacrifice yourself at the altar of Big Business, get yourself into bed with the only man you could think of who might be persuaded—by age-old means—to save the family business?'

She could not bear his sarcasm or stand his jeering eyes. She sat up and swung her legs to the floor, seeking with her feet the sandals Rosco had taken off in the course of his lovemaking.

He buttoned his shirt and fastened his belt, then pushed his hands into his pockets. He stood looking down at her drooping head. 'What exactly did that naïve mind of yours imagine would happen this afternoon? Did you in your innocence picture me lying in your arms, satiated with a surfeit of passionate loving, willing in my gratitude to grant your every wish?'

His scorn, his amusement at her expense, tore at her heart. Yes, she thought, that was exactly what I did imagine ... My word, I've grown up in the past quarter of an hour! My illusions have been taken one by one and smashed to pieces.

The tears she had struggled to hold back had their way and poured down her cheeks. She supposed it was a form of delayed shock, but whatever it was she could do nothing about it. She covered her face again, like a child trying to hide from a nasty picture in a story book.

'It's been such a strain,' she sobbed. 'I've worried myself sick. I just didn't know what to do for the best. All I know is I've been a total failure. I've—I've failed now even—even as a woman.' Her body shook with crying. 'If I'd been the son my parents really wanted,' she muttered, her voice thick with emotion, 'I would have pulled the business through.'

There was only the sound of her crying. 'My mother,' she went on, and she could not keep the bitterness from her voice, 'she wanted me to come and see you.'

'Does the business mean everything to her?' Rosco asked tonelessly. 'More than—anything in the world?'

'If you mean more than I do, the answer's yes—and no. It's not so much the business as—well, her way of life, her standard of living. I think secretly she's pleased no one wants to buy the house. I think secretly she blames me for—everything.'

'What is it you're after—a loan?' His voice sounded dead.

Lisette shook her head. 'You said yourself that wouldn't do any good. Not now, not with this new problem of wages.'

'I think we'd better go into the living-room.'

Rosco stood back to allow her to pass him. He had turned into a stranger. He indicated that she should sit down and she did so.

'Did your boy-friend condone your coming to my apartment today to—in a manner of speaking—solicit my help?'

She winced at the word with which he had chosen to describe the reason for her visit. 'He didn't know,' she murmured.

Rosco poured drinks and handed her a glass. She took it, looking up and thanking him, then shying away from his cold, impassive expression.

'If you don't want a loan, what do you want?' He drank, holding his glass and swilling the contents.

Lisette looked at him again and again their eyes clashed. She could not put her request into words, it was impossible after all she had said in the past.

He stared back at her unbelievingly. 'You're not after a takeover?'

It was as much as she could do to make herself nod. Then she cowered in advance of the onslaught.

'After your constant and—pardon me for saying so— monotonous condemnation of the whole idea of the takeover of smaller companies by bigger? After accusing giant corporations of crushing family businesses out of existence? And after saying that come what may, you wouldn't let *me* buy your firm, even if it was for sale?'

She rallied under his accusations and surprised herself by the re-emergence of her fighting spirit. 'What else is there left?' she asked, her voice rising. 'I tried asking the bank for a loan and had my request turned down. I tried the only other person I knew who might help. You. And *you* threw my request back in my face. You told me how emotionally I dealt with the problem and all because I was female, how I kept blurring the issue with my feminine approach. You couldn't see me except as a woman.'

Her heart pounded, her cheeks burned. 'Oh God, I wish I'd been the son my mother and father wanted! You would have treated me with respect, spoken to me man-to-man, as you did to Bob Farrell. Instead, you looked on me—you still do—as a kind of—of impostor, who had no right to be the head of a factory, puny and unprofitable though it may be.'

There was a long silence. Rosco stood with his back to her, staring out of the window at the traffic below.

She went on, 'I had already been forced to trample on my pride by asking you for a loan. Imagine how I feel today when I've had to ask you for more—much more than that.' She whispered, her voice husky with hopelessness and strain, 'Imagine how I feel now!'

He turned and looked at her. His face was blank, his eyes empty. 'I'll give you a lift to the railway station. It will save you taking the Underground.'

She said stiffly, 'There's no need for you to bother.'

'Nevertheless, I am bothering.' He found her coat and helped her on with it. His hands did not once touch her.

Was it possible, she thought in a daze as she descended the stairs from his apartment, that only a short time ago he had been making such intimate love to her she had nearly become his mistress?

He saw her to the platform from which her train departed. He did not wait for it to arrive. With a nod, he left her. Lisette had never felt so dejected and defeated in her life. Once again she had failed. Now she had no one to turn to, no one at all.

Lisette did not tell anyone about her visit to Rosco Hamden's flat. All the weekend she nursed her misery, pretending to her mother that she did not feel well.

Evelyn insisted that she should stay in bed and fussed around her, making her comfortable. Lisette did not object to her mother's concern. In a way she welcomed it. Since her father's death, she had worked at a pace that was not really hers. When she was a librarian, life had been tranquil. There had been no problems she could not solve, no fears of strikes or bankruptcy to contend with.

When Monday came, she was forced to admit that she was so drained of energy and hope that she could not face going to work. A few days' rest was what she needed, her mother said. A day or two at home, forgetting all about the factory, with herself to wait on her, and she'd soon be back to normal.

Lisette knew in her heart that her mother was right. She telephoned Bob, told him the trouble and asked if he would carry on in her absence. He readily agreed and assured her that he could manage the business perfectly well until she felt fit enough to return. Lisette smiled as she rang off. He even sounded eager to tackle the work! She was thankful that she had someone as reliable as Bob to act as her deputy.

Almost a week had gone before Lisette began to feel better. Every evening Bob had telephoned to report on the day's events. He sounded neither depressed nor cheerful, so Lisette assumed that no further demands had been made by the employees' union representatives that wage rates at the factory should be increased forthwith or there would be industrial unrest. She was thankful she had such a loyal work-force.

On Friday morning, the telephone rang and Evelyn answered. Lisette heard her say, 'Rosco! How nice to hear from you! How are you? When are we going to see you again?'

Lisette's heart, having leapt for joy, sank as she heard her mother's effusiveness.

'Lisette?' her mother was saying. 'No, she hasn't been well, but she's much better now. Yes, she's quite fit enough to speak to you.'

'No, Mother, no,' Lisette called in a hoarse whisper, 'I don't want to——'

'Lisette, dear,' Evelyn held out the phone, 'Rosco would like a word with you.'

She had ignored completely her daughter's furious shaking of the head. Lisette had no choice but to take the receiver. 'Yes?' she said in a colourless tone.

'Lisette? I hear you haven't been well. What's been wrong?'

You, she longed to say, I've been ill with you, with the futility of loving you, longing for you ... 'I don't know. Call it exhaustion.'

There was a short silence. 'Are you better now?'

'Yes, thank you.'

'Are you fit enough to travel?'

'You mean to London?'

'Yes. I want you to come and see me.'

There it was, the old imperious tone. Head of Emu products speaking, she thought with defensive scorn, chairman and managing director of Electro-Magnetic Universal. The words echoed in the great vacuum that had existed in her mind all that long, unhappy week.

'Well, can you manage it? This afternoon, I mean.'

Of course she could manage it, but some wilful imp leapt to life in her mind and she replied, 'I can't think of any reason why you should want to see me.'

She heard her mother at her elbow, urging, 'Go, dear, go and see him. Why not?'

'Look Lisette,' his tone was clipped, 'I want to see you. Today. Is that clear? Bring your mother with you, if you don't want to travel on your own. But I want to see you alone. Come at three o'clock. Can you manage that?'

'Yes,' she said mechanically, 'three o'clock.' The receiver crashed down at the other end.

Couldn't he have been pleasant? Didn't he possess any humanity? He had passion in abundance, she knew that only too well. But tenderness and consideration? No, none at all.

Lisette arrived early at Universal House. She had left home before lunch, promising her mother that she would have a meal somewhere, but she had not bothered. Her appetite had left her, swallowed up in her dread of coming face to face once more with Rosco Hamden.

She had racked her brains but had been unable to think of a reason for his wanting to see her. The magazine on her lap could not hold her attention. She closed it and went to the window, looking down at the traffic and the people in the street so far below.

Everything down there looked so small, she mused. Just as she, part-owner of an insignificant shoe firm, must look to Rosco Hamden from the pinnacle he occupied as chief executive of a giant electronics organisation. A conglomerate, he had called his company, a corporation which, he had said the day they had met, bought up businesses that were not necessarily in the same field as their own—in their case, electronics—but marketing quite different commodities and services, like bakeries, car hire, hotel chains ...

And what had she replied? She remembered ruefully. *I don't like monopolies. I don't like takeovers.* The words rang in her ears and mocked her.

How inexperienced she had been, how smug! What

blind faith she had had in her own power to overcome, singlehanded, any problems which might come her way in her life and her work. There was no doubt that she had grown up in the few short months since she had met Rosco Hamden.

'Mr Hamden will see you now, Miss Baird.' The voice of Rosco's secretary broke into her thoughts.

The executive suite seemed larger than she remembered and more impressive. The man lifting himself from an armchair to acknowledge her entrance seemed more intimidating. She felt dwarfed by the whole scene, unequal to whatever was to come. Maybe she was still feeling drained, maybe she should have postponed this interview, whatever it was about.

Rosco approached, his hand extended in a formal welcome. Had this man really made love to her—less than a week ago—with such ardour that she had been swept along by it almost to the point of complete surrender?

Their hands met, clasped and parted. It was all so impersonal Lisette wanted to cry. Now she was becoming emotional and 'womanly', she derided herself, everything, in fact, of which he had accused her the last time she had been in that room.

She looked around. There was still no desk, only armchairs and settees grouped around circular or rectangular tables for files and folders, for coffee cups and plates of biscuits.

This was the modern way, she supposed, where internal conferences took place, where heads of divisions and departments and their subordinates met for regular discussions of policy and progress and future plans.

This was a business world outside her experience. It bore no relation whatsoever to the empty inquiry desk and paper-strewn office floor, the wooden huts and leaking sheds that made up the premises of Baird Shoes.

She glanced at Rosco uncertainly. 'Sit down, Lisette.'
He indicated a chair beside his.

'Lisette'. Her heart jumped at his use of her first name. So he hadn't reverted completely to cold formality. There was, however, no warmth in his manner. His movements were brisk and businesslike, despite the way his eyes had scanned her face as their hands had touched.

'You still don't look fully fit. What's been wrong?'

She shrugged and sank into the armchair next to his, striving to hide the relief she felt at sitting down, endeavouring to keep her head upright instead of allowing it to rest against the chair back. 'I suppose,' she replied, 'it might be called the 'flu. Or any other name you might care to use.' She hoped she sounded offhanded enough to prevent any further probing on his part.

'It's not good practice,' he commented, seating himself, 'to let business worries reduce you to a state of prostration.'

'Business worries' he called it! If only it had been that, and not a face—his face—haunting her day and night, those words he had used about her mocking her, insulting her, resounding in her brain from the moment she awoke until she slept at night.

'Is that why you asked me here?' she challenged, 'to give me a lecture on business management?'

That faint smile touched his lips. It did not soften them. 'At least you haven't lost your spirit.'

'Implying that I've lost something else in your eyes?' He smiled but said nothing. He crossed his legs and clasped his hands loosely, completely at his ease. Did he never lose control of a situation? Lisette thought pettishly. Riled by his ability to relax, whereas she remained tense and apprehensive, she went on, 'My integrity, for instance?'

'So we're back to integrity, are we? I remember you attacked mine not so long ago.'

She stared down at her hands, remembering the occasion. It was when she had asked him for a loan.

He looked her over, taking his time. Only his eyes moved. His expensively-dressed, disturbingly attractive body was still, but it was clear from the animation in his eyes that his brain was functioning at full power.

He frowned as if puzzled. 'Haven't I seen that outfit you're wearing before?'

She wondered if he would remember the blue cord suit, and he had! She nodded. 'It was the last time I came here to see you. The same occasion as you mentioned just now, when I asked you for a loan to help save the factory from bankruptcy.' Should she remind him? Why not? 'You accused me of coming crawling to you on my hands and knees.'

'Ah, yes,' he said, rubbing his jaw thoughtfully.

'And you showed me the door.'

'Adding insult to injury, as they say. M'm, you'd hardly say there had been much—love lost between us, would you?' She clenched her hands to absorb the pain that swamped her body at his cynical words. 'Has there,' he mused, eyes closed, 'ever been a time during our comparatively short acquaintance when we haven't slung insults at each other?'

'I can—think of one or two,' she replied, clearing her throat to rid it of the sudden huskiness.

'Yes,' his eyes came half-open and rested on her face. He smiled as if the memory did not displease. 'So can I.'

'Why did you want to see me, Mr Hamden?'

He rose and she noticed he did not say, 'The name's Rosco,' as he had in the past.

He rested his palms on the back of his hips and regarded her tense figure. 'Despite our momentary digression into more—personal concerns, I invited you to see me for reasons that are strictly business.'

She looked up, puzzled. 'Strictly business?'

'That's what I said. You know nothing about it? You're unaware of what's been going on this past week you've been away?' She nodded, going a little cold. 'Hasn't your highly intelligent boy-friend told you anything of the week's events? No, I can see he hasn't, no doubt with a view to protecting you in your weakened state.'

Now she was really afraid. 'Protecting me? From what?'

'In the circumstances, I shall have to tell you. It seems that, last Monday afternoon, a deputation of your employees came to your office insisting on seeing you. Bob Farrell explained you were ill and that he was acting as your deputy. So they told him that either the increase in wages to bring them up to the negotiated union level took place next pay day—yesterday, to be precise—or they would stage a sit-in at the factory until that increase in wages was put into effect.'

'So,' Lisette put up a hand to her white cheeks, 'they're now on strike?'

'No. Moments after the deputation dispersed, and while your boy-friend and deputy, Bob, was standing hand to head, wondering what to do, he received another phone call.' He smiled. 'From your archenemy, Rosco Hamden, who expected to find you as usual at your worker-director desk.'

Lisette ignored the mockery and said, 'Well, what happened?'

In a move that might have been to tantalise, to keep her waiting, Rosco flicked a switch on the intercom. 'Coffee for two, please, Pamela.'

The reply, 'Certainly, Mr Hamden,' came clearly into the room.

'Please—tell me!'

He smiled at Lisette's pleading eagerness. 'Are you in torment, wanting to know what happened next?' He came to stand in front of her, pushing his hands into his pockets. A fleetingly serious look passed across his eyes. It went so quickly Lisette wondered if it had really been there. 'When I discovered you were ill at home, I was naturally worried, especially after what had happened between us a couple of days before.'

'You can get me off your conscience,' she responded tartly and she hoped, convincingly, 'it was exhaustion. Or 'flu—I told you.'

He lifted a shoulder. 'All right, it's as good a name as any. Anyway, I phoned to tell you and instead told Bob, that that morning I had called an emergency meeting of my company's Board of Directors. We discussed the plight of Baird Shoes. I explained the situation to them and it was decided that since the business was such a small one, any transaction that might take place between Electro-Magnetic Universal and the shoe company in question need not be put to the shareholders of E.M.U. for their approval or otherwise.'

Lisette felt bewildered. The room started reeling and she held her head. Pamela, Rosco's secretary, knocked and brought in the coffee. She heard him thank the girl and dismiss her. If he asks me to pour, Lisette thought, my hands are shaking so much I simply wouldn't be able to.

He did not ask her to pour. Instead, he filled the cups himself, adding cream and handing her the coffee and offering the sugar. Eagerly she sipped the hot liquid, while he settled himself down again and drank for a while in silence. When she had steadied, he seemed to know because he spoke again.

'I immediately instructed the company's auditors to go to your factory and inspect the books kept by Bob Farrell.'

Lisette dared not speak in case she broke the spell. Hope was rising within her like the dawn of a new bright day.

'The auditors arrived and while they were there, Bob was able to give some words of reassurance to your employees that, after all, all might not be lost. This kept them quiet, at least for the time being.'

The cup rattled against the saucer in Lisette's hand as she reached forward to put them on the coffee table. By then she was beyond caring about appearances, about letting her emotions show.

'Our auditors,' Rosco went on, his voice impersonal, 'found the books in impeccable order. Your Bob Farrell has much to recommend him.' This Lisette acknowledged with a nod. Useless to deny that Bob was 'hers'.

'Alas,' Rosco continued, 'Baird Shoes had very little to offer.'

Lisette stared. 'So——?' He did not answer. 'We're back where we were? No—no help, no hope at all?'

Rosco pulled himself from the depths of the chair, his hands feeling for his pockets again and he paced the area immediately around them. Then he stopped in front of her.

'Against any sane man's business judgment, Lisette,' he said, 'I'm going to make you an offer. Throw it back in my—or rather, my company's—face, if you like, but please, keep personalities out of it. I'm offering, on behalf of Electro-Magnetic Universal, to buy you out. Call it a takeover, call it what you will, I'm offering you a sum of money for Baird Shoes. Now,' he watched her closely, 'give me your answer. Yes or no?'

CHAPTER SEVEN

LISETTE placed her hands over her face. The world had spun like a top and she needed time to regain her balance.

'If you say "yes", Lisette, your worries will be at an end.' She still could not answer. 'I realise you're having a struggle. I know your abhorrence of takeovers, of family firms being swallowed whole by larger concerns. But the alternative is bankruptcy—our auditors assured us of this. Make your choice. Consult your mother, if you like.' She uncovered her face at last. 'There's the telephone,' Rosco said. 'Use it.'

She shook her head. 'No need. I know her opinion. I've made my decision.' Her body was growing warm, colour dyed her cheeks. 'It's yes, yes. Please!'

For the first time for weeks, she smiled. Her eyes came alive, they danced, they shone. Her smile illuminated her face as she gazed up at him. She wanted to throw her arms round his neck. The relief of feeling the responsibilities slide from her shoulders was almost too great be be borne.

He smiled at her reaction. 'Don't get too excited. You haven't heard the terms of the offer yet. You might not approve.'

He was right, of course. This was a business deal and called for more restraint. Before letting him see her relief and delight, she should have asked if there were any conditions attached and made a pretence of bargaining. She looked up at him, waiting, but determined even before he told her to accept the offer, no matter what it might be.

He laughed, throwing back his head, and her heart hammered. His mood was good, he was being human and approachable.

'You're a dead give-away, my girl. You're no business woman. I can read everything you're thinking in your face.' He reached out as if to touch her, seemed to change his mind and withdrew his hand. He continued his walk back and forwards. 'As you must realise, the buildings are mere shacks and worthless.' He looked towards her for a reaction. She compressed her lips and nodded.

He went on, 'The machinery now in use is so old, we would only receive from a buyer its value as scrap metal. The leathers you have in stock, the skins, the adhesives and the lasts might be saleable, but for a relatively small sum of money. I gather the land on which the premises stand is not leasehold, but freehold?'

Lisette nodded.

'Which means,' he said, 'that you own the land on which the factory stands. That is its greatest asset—the site. It's virtually the only thing on which we could raise any money in the deal. Now I'll tell you the sum of money we had in mind. I take it there are no shareholders, that you and your mother are the sole owners?'

'There's no one else,' she told him.

'Which simplifies matters considerably.' He then named a sum which, to her, sounded far in excess of what the factory was worth on the open market, even when the value of the site was taken into account. 'Does that satisfy you?'

'Rosco, it's wonderful!'

He laughed again. 'What unbusinesslike language! I must have that phrase recorded in the minutes of this meeting and report it to the Board of Directors of Emu products!'

Lisette's cheeks turned pink. She looked round the

room. 'You're probably having this conversation bugged, anyway, and taped on a concealed cassette recorder.'

'You're right, it's being taped,' he responded, and pointed to his head, 'here on a hidden recorder—by my brain.' Lisette smiled.

'So,' he walked towards her, 'it's a deal?' She nodded. He held out his hand. 'Shake on it.'

She extended her hand, too, but as their hands were about to meet, to her consternation he withdrew his. 'There is one point you've forgotten. A rather important point, in fact. Your mother. She's part-owner with you. You must get her approval.'

He was right again. Why was she acting so impulsively? Why could she not act the cool, poised business woman? She rose. 'I know my mother will approve, but I must let her know.'

'Don't speak for her, Lisette. She must do that for herself. I want to hear her verbal agreement before we go ahead and discuss the hand-over.'

He dialled her mother's number and held out the receiver. 'I'll listen on the extension. I take it you've no objection?'

'None at all.' As her mother answered, Lisette said eagerly, 'Mother? Our troubles are over. Rosco—I mean Emu products—well, to give them their proper name, Electro-Magnetic Universal—are buying us out.'

'Buying us out?' Lisette wondered why her mother's voice sounded strained. 'I'm not sure what you mean, dear?'

'I mean,' said Lisette, 'I mean Emu are—well, taking us over. I've—I've agreed.' There was a questioning silence. 'I thought you'd be pleased, Mother,' Lisette added, her voice wavering a little.

'But, dear, all we wanted was a loan. A takeover is surely too drastic? I mean, it's our company, isn't it? Your dear father started it, and he left it to us. He wouldn't have been happy to know that all his hard work has led to a—a takeover, when all we wanted was financial assistance.'

'Mother——' Oh, why, Lisette thought, couldn't her mother understand that a mere loan would no longer suffice? Why couldn't she accept that it was the end of Baird Shoes and that nothing whatever could save it now? 'Mother, we're broke, dead broke. I told you they wanted higher wages. The orders were running out. Anyway, they weren't being fulfilled ...'

'Dear, you should have told me money on its own couldn't save the business.'

Lisette could hardly stand the reproach. 'Mother,' she said desperately, 'I tried to explain. I thought you understood.'

'A loan, dear, a loan, that's all I thought you were going to ask for.'

Was her mother crying? Surely not! Not when she was too far away to be comforted. Lisette put her hand over the mouthpiece. 'I'm sorry,' she said to Rosco, 'I never dreamt it would be such a shock.'

'I'll handle this,' he said, holding the extension away from him. 'Put your phone down and wait in my secretary's office.'

Without questioning the authority in his voice—she was too stunned to question anything—Lisette obeyed.

Pamela looked up, said a cheerful 'Hallo, Miss Baird,' and asked her to take a seat. Then, to Lisette's relief, she carried on with her work.

Ten minutes later Rosco opened the door. 'Come in, Lisette.' He waited while she passed in front of him into the executive suite, then he confronted her.

'What the hell did you think you'd gain by not telling your mother the truth? Didn't you think she was old enough to be kept informed of *everything*?'

Lisette, stunned by her mother's reaction and also shocked by Rosco's reversion to his cold, authoritarian manner, could only falter, 'I did tell her the truth, even if it was only part of it. I—well, I just didn't want her to get hurt.'

'But, good heavens, girl, she had to know it all some time, and whenever that was, you must surely have known it would hurt. You should have told her the lot —about the unrest among the employees, the threatened strike, the bankruptcy looming up. Instead, you left it to me to do the dirty work for you.'

Lisette having felt so happy, had descended yet again to the depths. She told herself cynically, it was like being back home. She sank into a chair. 'So I've done it again, have I? In your eyes I've failed in my duty. Never mind,' her eyes lifted, challenging him, 'I'm used to the taste of failure.' She made a pretence of licking her lips. 'It's bitter and extremely unpleasant. But then you wouldn't know, would you?'

'Look, Lisette,' he grasped her wrist, drawing her up to face him, 'over the last few days, not to mention the last few minutes, I've been doing my utmost best for you. I've persuaded my Board of Directors that they were not entirely throwing their money away in buying out a nearly defunct business called Baird Shoes. And I've just informed your mother of the unpalatable facts and figures which so nearly forced Baird Shoes into liquidation. I've also managed—though God knows how—to talk her into a calmer frame of mind. With all due modesty, I really think I deserve not your sarcasm, but your gratitude.'

Lisette could not meet his eyes.

'Nor,' he went on, releasing her and watching her rub her wrist where his fingers had bruised her flesh, 'have you once thanked me.'

Her eyes widened. 'But I said——'

' "Rosco, it's wonderful." That's not thanks. You then went on to suggest that I might even be having our conversation secretly recorded. Was that thanks?'

And she had wanted to throw her arms round his neck! If only she had been at liberty to do so, how many barriers that would have broken down.

She shook her head helplessly. 'You've done so much for us, I don't know how to say thank you adequately. Just saying the words seems so insignificant when set against the generosity of all you've done.'

His eyes lingered on her for a moment, then he turned away.

'Rosco?'

'Yes?'

'What about the employees? What about their jobs?' She asked the question hesitantly, thinking she might arouse his anger again.

He turned to face her. 'As part-owner of the factory and therefore responsible for their means of livelihood, I wondered when you were going to think of your employees.'

His voice accused and she experienced a mixture of defiance and despair. 'So I'm in the wrong again. I can never do right in your eyes, no matter how much I try.'

His jaw hardened. 'Relax, girl. Do I have to calm you down, as well as your mother? Because if so, I'd choose a very different way.'

The look in his narrowed eyes had her pulses hammering. She felt a surge of longing for his soothing words, his touch and his caresses.

'Rosco,' she asked, 'will they lose their jobs?'

He gestured. 'Sit down again and I'll tell you what I have in mind.'

His company, he told her, owned an empty factory on an industrial estate to the north of London, not so many miles from where he lived. 'We could furnish it with up-to-date machinery for the manufacture of footwear,' he said, 'and, if the workers are willing to move house, they would be re-employed by us in more modern surroundings and conditions and much better rates of pay. If those carrots don't motivate them to move,' he added, 'nothing will.'

Lisette frowned. 'It would cost them money, selling their houses and buying new ones.'

'We'll even help them with that by giving them mortgages at special rates and also a resettlement allowance. Now,' with a taunting smile, 'perhaps you will acknowledge that there are *some* advantages in being employed by a giant company such as ours. Well,' he stood in front of her, 'are we going to have a political argument? If it ends in a stand-up fight, nothing will please me more.' She looked up and caught his grin. 'Fights between a man and a woman always end in victory—and conquest—for the man. That is, if he's the right sort of man.'

She smiled faintly and said uncertainly, 'Rosco? What about Bob?'

'He won't lose by the change.' His curtness cut off any further questioning on that subject.

'Is it possible,' she asked, 'for me to see the new factory some time?'

He smiled, his good humour restored. 'Sure. I'll take you there myself. I suppose you want to make certain the Baird "offspring" is going to a good home?'

She returned his smile and nodded.

'Are you free on Sunday? Come and have lunch with me, and I'll take you to the factory in the afternoon. I've got the key to the building.'

Her heart leapt. 'Are you sure? I mean, your weekends are precious, aren't they—the time when you relax?'

'Tell me, how better can a man relax than by having a good woman around?'

The cynical reply dimmed her pleasure just a little. 'A good woman', any woman.

'I'll even let you cook the lunch, if you want. And that's a real concession. There aren't many women I'd let mess about in my kitchen. You're one of the select few.'

Who, she wondered dismally, were the others? And how many women did he have? As many as he had moods, she supposed.

By the time she had reached home, her mother had become reconciled to the takeover.

'We'll be able to stay here,' she said. 'I'll inform the estate agent that we're withdrawing the house from the market. Oh, the relief, dear!' she sighed. 'To think we haven't got to pull up our roots ... I do hope you thanked Rosco for all he's done for us?'

With a twinge of conscience, Lisette nodded. She had thanked him—but only when he had prompted her to do so.

She phoned Bob to tell him the good news, but he told her he already knew. Rosco had called him as soon as she had left and had had a long talk with him.

'You've done well, Lisette,' said Bob. 'I honestly didn't think Electro-Magnetic would be in the least interested in a firm as small as ours. I don't know how you talked Mr Hamden round to doing what he's done.'

Lisette blushed at the memory of her planned 'seduction' of Rosco, and how wrong it had gone. How could she have thought that an innocent like herself might have used such an old and very feminine trick to trap a man like Rosco Hamden into the takeover of a business which was so plainly a loser? So why had he done it?

The next day passed slowly. When she had told her mother that she would be going to Rosco's for lunch and then he would be taking her to see the new factory, her mother did not comment, except to say, noncommittally, 'How nice, dear.'

It was plain that she suspected no other motive for the visit, no deeper relationship developing between them. And her mother was right. It was really a business lunch, with the difference that, provided Rosco was in the right mood, he would let her cook the meal herself!

He was in that 'right mood', it seemed. From the way he greeted her on the threshold of his flat, and judging by the casual way he was dressed, he was in a very different mood from the hard-hitting, quick-thinking image he presented during working hours. He wore dark blue slacks and his honey-coloured silk shirt was high-necked.

Lisette was glad she had dressed in the same casual fashion. Her jeans and blue tee-shirt caught his eyes and his gaze wandered lazily over her shapely figure. She remembered the scarlet outfit the girl called Wanda had worn the day she had visited Rosco unexpectedly to beg for a loan. She also recalled the blonde hair and perfect features.

'It's no good,' she said, prickling under his amused regard, 'trying to compare me with your beautiful girlfriend. I'm in a different class from her.' His smile broadened and she went on defensively as he closed the door, 'If you'd wanted sophistication, sexiness and—and experience, you should have invited her, not me.'

'Well, well. All that self-denigration and I haven't spoken a word yet, not even "Hallo". What are you all steamed up about?'

'I'm not steamed up. But you didn't seem to approve of the way I'm dressed.'

His hand grasped her shoulder and he turned her. 'How do you know,' he said, smiling, 'that I was looking *at* your clothes and not *through* them?' He laughed at her expression. 'I've shocked you! You must surely be a collector's item—a girl, probably the only one of the species left, who can be shocked by a veiled reference to the nakedness beneath her clothes. Would you like a drink?'

Confused by the intimate overtones of his comments,

she answered, 'Yes, no—yes, please.' She sat in an arm-chair and waited, trying to relax.

He poured and handed her a glass. 'The "sherry before lunch" routine,' he commented. 'I bet it's a ritual you don't indulge in in your household. It would go against your proletarian principles.'

'Why do you keep sneering at my compassionate attitude to the under-privileged?'

He came to sit on the arm of her chair and rested his arm across her shoulders. She jerked irritably at what was plainly a placatory action. 'Is that how you interpret my remarks? If so, I'm sorry. I'm compassionate to the less fortunate section of society, too. If I weren't, why did I come to the rescue of a poverty-stricken family business?'

Lisette said nothing. He was so clever at winning their verbal battles. He never failed.

'Do you know something, my little worker-director? I speak to you as I speak to no other woman. None of my other women acquaintances would understand what the hell I was talking about. But you,' he curled a finger under her chin and turned her face upwards, 'you're so intelligent, you understand everything I say without my having to explain it afterwards in words of one syllable.'

'"He loved her for her intelligence."' She quoted the classic joke bitterly.

He lowered his head and brushed her lips. 'Why,' he said softly, 'would you like me to "love" you for—something else?'

She eased her chin from his hold and stood up, pushing in her tee-shirt which had come adrift. 'If you'll tell me where the food is——'

The deep freeze was in the kitchen and she helped herself to items which she placed in the oven for the specified time. It was good to work in such a well-equipped, clinically clean kitchen. She wondered who kept the place so spotless. A daily help, she guessed, a lady who probably did all the things a wife would have done if Rosco Hamden had at any time seen fit to take one.

But, she thought, placing plates in the hot cupboard of the electric cooker, no woman could exist who would suit *every* mood of the head of Emu products. Which was why, she thought, clattering the dishes extra loudly, he had such a selection of women friends—all the more to choose from when a certain mood came over him.

'What's biting you?' She swung round, red-faced, to see him straddling a kitchen chair. In her fit of temper, she hadn't heard him come in. 'Why all the noise?' he asked. 'It was you who chose to cook the lunch. I didn't force you.'

'It's nothing to do with the lunch,' she said. 'It was——' She hesitated. She couldn't tell him the truth! 'It was something I was thinking, that's all. Nothing to do with you,' she lied quickly, sensing he was about to question her further.

'Next time,' he said, as his eyes wandered to her tight-fitting jeans, 'remind me to buy you an apron. I'd like to see you as the efficient little housewife you'll become after you're married to Bob Farrell.'

'How do you know,' she fenced, dishing up the meal, 'I shall get married?'

'You mean,' his eyebrows surely could not go any higher! 'you would consider dispensing with the marriage ceremony? Even you, with your high principles and slightly straitlaced response to a man's love-making?'

'It's going on all the time nowadays, isn't it?' she replied defensively, but not meaning a word of what she was implying. 'You should know, shouldn't you? Your private life——'

'Is my business.' He stood. 'It's time we ate.'

'Anyway,' Lisette said, as they seated themselves on

144

stools at the breakfast bar which ran along one wall of the kitchen, 'Bob Farrell——'

'Doesn't matter. You've already told me. And I don't believe you. A nicer young man you couldn't hope to meet.'

She turned to look at him as they sat side by side. 'You're talking to me like a father,' she said, flashing him an impish look.

'A *father*?' He seized his knife as if it were a weapon. 'Much more of that, you impudent young female, and I'll——'

'Shall we eat?' she asked, with wide-eyed innocence.

'You're a cheeky little devil,' he murmured, filling his mouth with food.

Rosco's flat was on the edge of the country, not far from Epping Forest. The factory owned by Emu products was a short car journey away on an industrial estate in a London suburb.

'There's nothing in it,' Rosco told her as he parked the car outside a newly-constructed red-brick building. 'It's empty. All you'll be seeing is bricks and mortar.'

Lisette shook her head, her eyes bright. 'I shall be seeing the future. A dream which has become reality.'

He gave her a curious look as he locked the car and escorted her to the building, opening the glass swing door with a key and motioning her in. Even the entrance lobby was, by Baird Shoes standards, spacious.

'Inquiry desk,' Rosco said with a smile. 'Nobody there, just like yours. But I promise you there will be before very long.'

On the ground floor was a vast room with many windows, through which the sunlight streamed, making patterns on the tiled floor. Lisette half-closed her eyes and visualised machinery and work benches and people.

'The whole building is air-conditioned,' Rosco

remarked, 'and, needless to say, centrally heated.'

'So the smells connected with the work won't hang around but will be extracted without everyone getting frozen by opened windows? That's wonderful!'

On the first floor, there was a repeat of the large ground floor room. 'For expansion,' said Rosco, 'when —not if—it happens.'

The third floor was divided into rooms of varying sizes, the large areas plainly intended to accommodate typists and clerical assistants, the smaller rooms to be used by the management staff and personnel department. One room seemed more important than the others. Leading from it, through a communicating door, was a smaller office, no doubt intended for a secretary.

Lisette, dreamy-eyed, wandered back into the main room and gazed from the window. All around there were buildings similar to the one they were in, some even now only half-built.

She turned, leaning back against the sill. 'I think I'll have this room. There's a—well, a kind of nice feel about it. Would I——' she looked at Rosco, 'would I have a secretary?'

He looked back at her seriously for a few moments, then he laughed. 'Of course the manager will have a secretary. No shortage of money, remember?'

She walked about, her arms wrapped around her, still unable to believe that in a few months she would be working there instead of the tumbledown shack which contained her office at the present Baird Shoe factory.

'Rosco?'

'Yes?' He answered her absently, turning from the window to which he had wandered.

'Once you said you would give me lessons on management. Will you keep that promise? You have such a wide experience of industry, you must know an awful lot about management.'

He walked towards her, arms folded. 'I'll teach you, if that's what you want. I'll charge you,' he teased, unfolding his arms and wrapping them round her waist. 'The form of payment, my sweet one, won't be in money.'

She frowned, drawing herself in. 'Rosco, I didn't mean that. I——'

'Don't worry,' he said softly, 'I won't ravish you. Not without invitation, anyway. When do we start? Next weekend? Are you free on Saturday?'

'I think so. Shall I come to you, or——?'

His arms, still encircling her waist, seemed content to stay there and she relaxed under his hold. 'Let me think. I've got it, we'll do it the easy way. We'll go to Epping Forest—it's only a short distance from here—and take a picnic lunch. Weather permitting, that is. If it's raining, we'll have to think again.'

'What about books? Will you take them with us?'

'Books?' He laughed down at her. 'I won't need books. It's all in my head. Naturally, I'll tell you some books to read.' He took her hand in his. 'Seen enough? Satisfied?'

'More than satisfied. It's far better than I expected.'

'So the head of Electro-Magnetic isn't such a villain?' he smiled, leading the way down the stairs and locking the door after them. They walked to his car. 'So "big" isn't so "bad" and "small" isn't so "beautiful"?'

She shrugged. He was taunting her with her own words and it was an uncomfortable feeling.

At the car he took her by the shoulders and gave her a small shake. 'Admit it.'

The factories all around were quiet because it was Sunday. Only one or two people walked to and fro, disappearing into buildings.

'I admit it,' she said, 'but reluctantly and only because in the circumstances I can hardly do otherwise.'

He laughed, his eyes glad that he had won the argument. He drew her close and kissed her. 'That was the long awaited "thank you" kiss you never gave me. Except that I took it from you. Get in the car. I'll drive you back to my flat.'

Rosco made a pot of tea for them both and found an unopened packet of coconut cookies. Lisette drank her tea and rested in the armchair, eyes closed, deeply content.

She must have slept because she became conscious of hands taking hers and holding them until her eyes came open. Rosco's eyes gazed into hers and it seemed to be evening outside. It was not getting dark, but the birdsong sounded different.

Rosco pulled her up and into his arms. 'I've sat here for an hour and a half watching the Sleeping Beauty. And all that time my appetite has grown. Not so much for food, my sweet, as for——' His lips, parting hers, finished the sentence.

His hands found the separation of her tee-shirt from her jeans. They roamed over the softness of her midriff, around her back and all over the enticing curves her body possessed. She clung to him as he brought her to life. From the dreams of her sleep she was entering another dream—that his lovemaking came not from desire but love.

'Stay with me,' he whispered, spreading his kisses over her throat as her head hung back, 'stay here tonight, Lisette. I'll teach you my needs, my desires. I'll show you how to respond to a man's passions.'

'Rosco, I—I wish I could say how much I——' No! She must not tell him how deeply she loved him. He was not interested in love, only in the appeasement of his desire. But she loved him so intensely, she wished to please him in whatever way he wanted ...

'You want to stay?' His eyes blazed with gladness. 'Is that what you're trying to tell me?'

The door bell rang, once, twice, three times. He let her go and ran his hand through his hair. The bell rang again, insistently, as though someone was refusing to remove the pressing finger until there was an answer.

'I'll go,' said Lisette, and walked unsteadily across the room and into the small entrance hall.

Wanda stood on the doorstep. The tables had been turned. Last time they met, Wanda had opened the door to find a scared, vulnerable girl standing there. Now that same girl, no longer scared, but still painfully vulnerable, was on the inside, while Rosco's woman—as Lisette herself had so nearly become—was the outsider.

Wanda's eyes roved insolently over Lisette's dishevelled figure, then moved to Rosco who had come into the hall.

'Good God, darling,' she said, 'you must be hard up for a woman if you had to make use of a tee-shirted, jean-clad overgrown student-type!'

She entered and dropped her jacket on to a chair. This time her step-in trouser suit was made of black velvet. A diamond brooch glittered on the lapel.

'If you were so desperate for a woman, darling,' she went on, 'why didn't you call me? I'd have come at the click of your fingers.' She leant against him, pressing close to his body. He did not repel her. 'Like I always do.' She looked up at him.

Lisette walked past them, found her handbag in the living-room and returned to the hall. Rosco thrust Wanda from him and went across to Lisette, who stood at the entrance door. Wanda, with a small laugh, left them.

'Thanks for today,' was all Lisette could find to say. She was too choked for words. Much more and the tears would be spilling over.

'I'll ring you,' he said. He was remote again, a stranger. He made no attempt to explain or excuse.

Lisette supposed he was used to such a situation, with one woman arriving before another left.

'There's no need.' She tried to keep her voice cold, but some of her misery crept in.

'Next Saturday,' he said.

'Forget it,' she responded. 'I'd hate you to get your dates mixed again.'

'I didn't invite her.'

'You don't need to, do you? You're unmarried, free of all moral obligations. Your mistress can come and go as she likes, can't she?'

His arm lifted in a sharp movement. Lisette thought he was going to hit her. She turned and ran down the three flights of stairs and felt the cool evening air sweep across her burning cheeks.

Lisette told Bob about her visit to Rosco's flat. He showed no sign of concern, let alone jealousy, that she had spent the day with another man.

She supposed that since Rosco Hamden was soon to be their employer, Bob regarded it as nothing unusual that he should want to see Lisette to talk business.

He seemed more interested in the fact that Rosco had shown her the new premises which would house the factory. He questioned her closely as to its design and even asked her to make a sketch of the place. With this in his hands, he began working on the possible placing of machinery, the allocation of offices, the space that could be used for the storage of materials.

Lisette told him, too, about her proposed visit to Rosco the following Saturday and the reason for that visit. 'But I've decided not to go after all,' she said, omitting to tell him why.

She could not bring herself to be in the close company of a man who, with such calmness and absence of embarrassment, was able to switch his passion and invitation to a night of lovemaking from one woman to another.

'You must go,' Bob urged. 'It's a great opportunity for you to learn at first hand all about management—modern management. Where else would you get such a wealth of information? Only by attending evening lectures, and that's a lengthy business.'

So, when Rosco telephoned, as he had promised, to confirm their arrangement, Lisette did not have the pleasure of throwing his invitation back in his face. She was glad afterwards that she had not done so. It would have revealed a weakness, letting him know that she was upset about Wanda's arrival at his flat.

In any case, she could not have refused him. He phoned her during office hours and his manner was cool and detached. He was very much the boss of an international electronics organisation. He would meet her, he said, at the entrance to the Underground station and they would carry on from there.

'Don't worry about the food,' he said. 'We'll either eat out—if the weather's bad—or I'll have some sandwiches made up.'

'Thank you,' she said, feeling annoyingly nervous. 'It's very kind of you to take all this trouble.'

'Isn't it?' he said dryly, and rang off.

The weather was warm, but a few clouds hung in the sky. Lisette wore jeans as on her last visit to him. They were brand new and not frayed at the hem as the others had been. Her top was red and ribbed and round-necked. She wondered if Rosco saw her as an 'overgrown student-type' as his lady friend had so scathingly referred to her.

He showed no sign of noticing how she was dressed when he leant across to open the passenger seat of the car outside the station. His greeting was cool and unsmiling. Had he not forgotten the way they had parted the weekend before? His skin was tanning from the warm sun they had had for the past week or two. His navy blue shirt was partly unbuttoned, his dark slacks drawn in to his lean waist with a dark blue belt.

His hair looked newly-washed and there was about him a tantalisingly fresh, hard masculine look which had Lisette's senses stirring restlessly. Now she was with him again, her body began to shed the strange depression that had shackled her actions from the moment she had left him six days before. He, however, seemed to regard her as no more than a passenger in his car. It hurt her deeply to think that, even after the intimacies they had on occasion shared, he could still look upon her as just another woman.

'Where are we going, Rosco?' Lisette asked in a small voice.

'I told you, to Epping Forest. Have you heard of it? It has a long history. Once it was much bigger than it is now. In Roman times an enormous forest stretched across East Anglia from the River Thames to the Wash, but now only small pieces of that forest remain. One of them is the few thousand acres of Epping Forest.'

They left the town of Epping behind and the road took them through the forest itself. It was a main road full of traffic and it was plain that the forest was a popular place for weekend family outings.

Lisette glanced up through the windscreen and saw how the branches of the trees met overhead, forming an elongated archway. Above the trees the sun gilded the leaves and in the spaces between, the sun burst through, making the drivers and their passengers shield their dazzled eyes.

'If you're lucky,' Rosco commented, overtaking a slow-moving vehicle, 'you might see a deer moving through the trees.'

'In this part of the world?' Lisette asked, surprised. 'So near to London?'

Rosco nodded. 'Fallow deer, they're called. Direct descendants of the fallow deer of England. They're distinct from the South European deer found in many parks. The fallow deer in Epping Forest are almost unique in Britain. Sometimes they shoot across the main road, and you can imagine how dangerous that is, not only for the deer but for the motorists. Hence the warning notices at the side of the road.'

They drove on and Rosco motioned towards the forest across the road. 'High Beach,' he said. 'If you walk a short distance, you'll find the ridge from which you can see for miles across Hertfordshire.'

A short time later, he slowed the car and bumped off the road on to a forest clearing, coming to a stop in a parking area. 'Here we are. Our destination—Connaught Waters. Out you get and I'll lock the car.'

From the boot of the car he pulled a holdall, then he took Lisette's hand and drew her after him. They walked through the trees towards the lake. Not far away, at the lakeside, was the boat-house with a few rowing boats moored nearby. On the lake other boats holding one or two people were moving steadily, oars dipping, rising and leaving a skimming trail.

Lisette tripped over a tree root and Rosco steadied her, unlinking their hands and putting his arm about her shoulders. She looked up at him questioningly, her heart beating fast. Was his aloof mood leaving him and a new, warmer mood taking its place? Did she suit this mood better than the other? He did no more than smile down at her and look ahead. The excitement she had begun to feel died away.

There were families gathered in circles, cloths spread on the ground and covered with flasks and cups and paper plates. Other people gazed across the water, their backs against tree trunks. Here and there couples lay, entwined and in their absorption with each other, heedless of the comings and goings around them.

Lisette looked at them with envy. It was a sensation she had never known—to be so admired and desired by a man she loved that, when she was with him, the whole world receded into a meaningless blur.

Rosco found a small clearing a short distance from the water's edge, where the weekend crowds had gathered. He drew an old raincoat from the holdall and spread it on the ground. Then he passed the holdall to Lisette.

'You be mother.'

She laughed back at him and caught her breath at the flare of warmth that lit his eyes. To hide her embarrassment she raked in the holdall and found packets of sandwiches, tomatoes, fruit and biscuits.

'I made the sandwiches,' he informed her, stretching out his legs and leaning back on his elbows. 'I hope you're not a fussy eater and that you like the fillings.'

'*You* made them? I didn't think you had it in you!' she returned.

He sat up and rubbed his hands together slowly. 'Many more remarks like that, young woman, and you'll finish up across my knee! Nothing would give me greater pleasure than to spank you into submission. Ever since I've known you, you've been far too cheeky——'

Her head swung round. With relief, she saw the smile. He didn't mean it, he was joking.

'Why shouldn't I say what I think?' she challenged, offering him a sandwich. He took two. 'We're on the same level, you said so once yourself. You're the head of a large company, I'm the head of a small company. So we're equals. Aren't we?' She gazed at him, demanding an answer.

He looked at her and looked away. He said thoughtfully, 'M'm,' adding, 'let's eat.'

They finished their meal and packed away the empty flask, having drained it of the coffee it had contained.

Rosco lay back, his linked hands supporting his head. Lisette hugged her knees.

'It's so pleasant here,' she said, looking about her.

'The lake isn't natural,' Rosco told her. 'Once the area was just marshland. The lake was made in the eighteen-eighties. They called the lake Connaught Waters after the Duke of Connaught, who was appointed by Queen Victoria to be the first ranger of Epping Forest. In a really cold winter the lake freezes and people come here to skate.' He was silent for a few moments. 'I used to spend hours here as a boy, fishing and boating. I loved the place. Still do. We lived a bus ride away.'

She wanted to hear him talk of his childhood but did not like to question him. Instead she asked, 'Can we go and look at the lake now?'

'Not yet. This is a talkabout, not a walkabout.' She laughed and he lifted his head to look at her. 'You know, it's a strange thing,' he gazed narrow-eyed at the blue sky between the overhead branches, 'but we've been together for over an hour and we haven't quarrelled once.'

'I hate quarrelling with you,' she said brightly. 'I'd much rather we were friends.'

His head came up again and she coloured deeply, regretting her revealing words. 'I'm willing,' he said, his hand groping for her, 'more than willing.'

She evaded him, saying hastily, 'Tell me about management.'

'What do you want to know?'

'Oh,' she lifted her shoulders, 'everything.'

'Everything? Oh, in that case, it will only take me a couple of minutes!' She laughed with him and he added, 'No one but a fool takes on part-time lecturing for nothing. I shall demand payment.'

Lisette moved uncomfortably, knowing he wanted her to ask him what he meant, but she stayed silent.

'Let me see now,' he murmured, sitting up and linking his hands round his knees, 'the subject is so enormous I find it difficult knowing where to start.' He stared unseeingly into the depths of the forest.

Lisette gazed at the way his hair tapered to the shape of his head. She saw the breadth of his back, the shoulder blades pushing against the thin shirt fabric. His sleeves were rolled to above his elbows and his arms were tanned, the dark hairs spreading beyond the gold band of his watch to his wrists. She felt a stab of desire, wanting to stroke the back of his head, to run her fingers down his arms.

At last he spoke. 'In industry,' he said, giving her a smile touched with sarcasm, 'there are eighty per cent advisers and only twenty per cent doers. You'll find an "adviser" behind piles of paper. That's the only way he can justify his existence.'

'But what about management?'

'Have patience, woman. I'm coming to that. A good manager,' he went on, narrowing his eyes in thought, 'must have one vital quality—he must be able to get people involved, he must train them to work as a team. Today, work enrichment is the thing. Workers are regarded as individuals nowadays. The "conveyor belt" mentality is finished. It's all small teams now, more group working.'

'What about the manager?' Lisette said in a small voice.

'This is management,' he said with a touch of irritation, 'which is what you wanted to know about, isn't it? The manager is more of an adviser now, not so much a boss. There's less management by control, more by motivation. Workers are no longer treated like kids and naughty kids at that, and they have the "behaviourists" and social scientists to thank for that step forward.' He looked at her, but she knew he did not really see her. 'Are you with me?'

She nodded.

'In large organisations there's been a revolution in managerial thinking. We know now that you have to trust people to get the best out of them. Managers nowadays have to be prepared to relinquish the tight control they used to have, to hand that control over to those who are doing the job.'

Again he gazed into the distance, but Lisette knew he was not seeing the trees, the worn paths, the occasional dog which strayed near them, snuffling the ground.

'Nowadays,' he went on, 'it's discussion, not negotiation; involving workers in the decision-making process, encouraging them to do things voluntarily instead of under pressure. All this takes time.' He flicked her a glance and looked away. 'It takes patience, years of discussion. The right personality of those at the top is an absolute essential. They must have a very high standard of leadership—of the *new style*.'

As he spoke, Lisette realised that, although she had been running the family business for over a year, she really knew very little about the job she had taken on. It was essential before tackling the managership of a brand new factory, such as they were being given, to read a great many books on the subject.

'Had enough or do I go on?' Rosco had become aware of her again.

She nodded. 'Enough for the moment, thanks. I'm beginning to understand what you meant when you said the subject was enormous. But I'm really interested. I should love to learn some more.' His raised eyebrows put her on edge. 'That is, if you don't mind teaching me some more some time.'

'The pleasure would be all mine,' he said dryly, lying full length again. 'I haven't even scratched the surface of the subject matter.'

She wrapped her arms about her knees again and

stared around her, hearing the birds singing, seeing them lift off from branches, spread their wings and flutter to land a few trees distant. 'I'm going to look at the lake,' she said, rising and dusting her legs free of leaf mould. She wandered off, climbing the steep bank which brought her through the trees to the water's edge.

She glanced back once, hoping Rosco was following. He had remained where he was, seeming to have forgotten her. Disappointment gripped her, although she told herself she was foolish to expect him to act the friend, let alone the lover, running after her as if every moment spent without her was wasted.

On impulse, she slipped off her sandals and stepped into the cool water, pulling the legs of her jeans clear. With eyes that were unaccountably sad, she watched the laughing couples in boats on the lake. The young men rowed while their girl-friends caught handfuls of water and let it run away. Again that envy welled up. It was something else she had never known—complete accord with a man, a sharing of laughter, the simple joy of being together, hand-in-hand companionship.

The water swished round her ankles as the wash of the boats reached her. She thought of the man lying alone in the clearing between the trees. If she never returned to his side, would he even notice? He had his own girl-friend, a beautiful woman called Wanda. Why should a simple, uncomplicated girl like herself—a girl who, for her parents' sake, should have been born a boy—matter to Rosco Hamden?

She slipped her wet feet into her sandals and went back to his side. He did not even open his eyes as she lowered herself beside him. Her feet were still wet and she looked around for something with which to dry them.

'Rosco?'

'Yes?'

'Have you got a towel?'

'A towel? What do you think I am? A nursemaid?'

A little plaintively, 'My feet are wet.'

'You shouldn't have paddled.'

So he had watched her! 'I couldn't resist it.'

'Nor could I, as a boy.' He sighed as if moving was a nuisance. He pulled his handkerchief from his trouser pocket. 'Here you are.'

She dried her feet and said, 'I'll take it home and wash it.'

'No. Put it back in my pocket.'

She did, pushing it down so that it would not fall out. Beneath her hand she felt the hardness of his hip and for a few seconds her hand lingered. She could not explain why, she had never done such a thing before.

His head lifted and he looked at her through narrowed eyes. She snatched her hand away and his head rested back again. He had unbuttoned his shirt and pulled it free of his belt. At the sight of him lying there, from head to foot a magnet, Lisette had to quell her instinct to reach out and trail her fingertips over his skin.

She tore at the grass beside her, finding a piece to chew, then discarding it, hating its bitter taste. She pulled at the neck of her ribbed top, wishing she had worn a cool shirt. She curled up on one side, then on the other.

'Stop fidgeting, woman, for heaven's sake,' Rosco growled.

'I can't,' she said.

His head came up again, a sardonic eyebrow rose, but he lay back, saying nothing.

She looked at him, her head movements jerky. 'Rosco?' He murmured in reply. 'There's—there's an insect hovering over you. It's landed on your chest!'

'Brush it away,' he said lazily.

She dived and her hand skimmed over the dark hairs,

removing the insect which flew away. But her hand was trapped, swatted and pinned down. The insect had escaped. It was her hand that was the prisoner.

His hand held hers against him. Under her palm she felt the roughness, and under that the hardness of the bone structure beneath his chest. She tensed.

'Please let my hand go, Rosco.'

'Why should I? It's what's been bugging you this past half-hour, or maybe longer for all I know—the fact that I've ignored you.' His eyes stayed closed but his faint smile was full of knowledge. 'You just couldn't stand it, could you? You just couldn't keep still. You were determined somehow to get my attention.' He jack-knifed upright, caught her shoulders, twisted her round and pulled her down on top of him. 'Well, you've got it now. What are you going to do with it?'

Her wrists were caught in grips of iron and he held them out straight at each side so that she was spread-eagled and helpless against him. To keep her face from touching his, she had to place an unbearable strain on her neck, holding her head at an unnatural angle.

They stayed thus for some moments. His eyes were taunting her and full of laughter, not in a kindly way, but as if he knew the agony she was going through to keep herself away from him.

It was no use, in the end the strain was too great and her head flopped forward. Instead of turning his head so that their cheeks touched, Rosco stayed as he was and their lips met.

Still with her arms imprisoned, Lisette felt his mouth move, forcing hers open. There was nothing she could do but let him have his way.

'Now she's kissing me,' he murmured against her mouth.

Indignantly she lifted her head again. 'No, I'm not! It's you who kissed me.'

He laughed, his eyes brilliant. 'What, in this position, with you pinning *me* down!'

'You pulled me on top of *you!*' she retorted. 'I didn't——'

The sentence was never finished. Her wrists were released but arms clutched her, rolled her on to her back and she was pinned beneath his weight, full-length and helpless. His body was hard and overwhelmingly masculine, in his eyes the determination to catch and conquer, to master and subdue.

'This is the second time I've got you where I want you,' he said, through his teeth. She struggled, but he held her still with ease. 'We're beginning to know each other very well indeed, aren't we, Miss Lisette Baird? What would your "understanding boy-friend" say about that?'

'I told you,' she said, trying to evade his seeking mouth, 'he doesn't matter. I——'

'He doesn't matter?' he gritted. 'It's all right by me, my pretty. If you have it in mind to play around with one man while keeping another trailing obediently after you on a lead, then don't let me change your plans, especially as it seems I'm the one you're intending to play around with.' His mouth settled, taking hers by surprise. His kiss was as harsh as his tone of voice. His ungentle hands searched out the agonisingly vulnerable places on her body.

She had to free her mouth to speak, she had to tell him how wrong he was about her. With an immense jerk she freed her mouth from his pitiless lips.

'Rosco,' she gasped, 'Rosco——' It was essential to find some breath to enable her to talk. Her hands came up to hold each side of his head.

At her touch he was still. She felt the pressure of him all over her and wished that the desire she was aware that he was experiencing stemmed from love instead of mere proximity. Any girl could do this to a man, she thought in anguish, any female form beneath a man's moulding hands could arouse sexual appetite.

But love? That was different. She searched his eyes as they looked into hers. Where was the love? It wasn't there, was it? There was only a frightening kind of cruelty, a curious wish to punish, a biting, un-illusioned cynicism. What had she done to infuse him with these negative, corrosive emotions? It was as if, in some strange way, she had let him down ...

'Please, Rosco, let me tell you something.' Her fingers, still against his head, started to move gently through his hair. 'I'm not at all the kind of person you think I am.' She could feel his breath fanning her mouth. Her eyes explored his face and she saw faint laughter lines pencilled by time around his eyes, a frown mark forming between his brows. She smiled slightly, making no attempt to hide her feelings.

If it was there in her look, that love she felt for this dynamic, restless man, she did not care. Why should she hide it now that she desired him as much as he desired her, even though their desire was built on very different foundations?

If she were to give herself, it could only ever be in love. She loved him and had done so for longer than she could calculate. If he wanted her, as it seemed he did, then why should he not take her?

'Explain what you mean,' he said softly, not only tolerating her stroking hands but seeming to like it.

'It's difficult,' she whispered, 'but—well, I've never wanted any man to touch me before. Always I've wanted to draw back, move away, and if that wasn't possible, I've gone stiff and tense.'

'It hadn't escaped my notice,' he said, with a faint smile.

'No, no, you're wrong. Not with you. If I have gone tense it was because—well, because I knew——' she took a deep breath, 'I knew what you would do to me.'

'And what have I—done to you?' he murmured, turning and kissing her wrist near his face.

'Broken down all my barriers, the—the inhibitions which have built up over the years.' Her hands went to his shoulders. She closed her eyes. It was not possible to watch the change which would come over him when she told him the truth. 'It's only been your touch that I've not only tolerated but actually wanted and—and welcomed.'

When her eyes opened, she steeled herself for his pity. It was not pity she saw but pleasure, satisfaction —and something else she could not fathom.

'I don't know if you're aware of what you're telling me,' he said, his body hard with a desire that demanded indulgence, 'but I'm assuming you know what you're saying, that your powers of reasoning are unimpaired and that you also know—and welcome—what's coming your way.'

His head lifted. He searched her face for rejection. Finding none, his mouth took possession of hers. Irritated by the barrier formed by her tee-shirt, he tugged at it, loosening it and slipping impatient hands inside.

Lisette's skin tingled as his caresses, with a sweet familiarity, skimmed and stroked, bringing her to vibrant life. Her body moved and responded with delight to his lovemaking and her arms curled and crossed around his neck. His lips made their way to the hollows of her throat, feathering back again to settle with hard, intimate possession on her parted lips.

'By heaven,' he murmured, 'if we weren't in a public place, there'd be no holding me back, you little minx. There'd be no nonsense from you this time about stopping as there was last. I'd have my way and you'd belong to me, from the top of your sweet head to your wriggling toes. You'd be my woman, minx.'

Her body came exquisitely alive under his increasingly possessive touch. She moaned and hid her face in his neck. 'Rosco,' she whispered, 'please——'

'We'll wait,' he agreed, 'but I say it reluctantly. For the present, however, I'll tame my desire—it won't be easy—and wait.' He moved on to his side, pulling her round, then he smiled into her eyes and kissed her. He tidied her tee-shirt, pushing it into place under the waistband of her jeans. It was an act that told of a growing knowledge of her, of an intimacy between them that increased with every caress.

He took her into his arms and they lay together, wrapped about in each other, her head on his shoulder, his cheek against her hair. There was a contentment about her now; no longer was she tormented by a driving longing. She was at peace—with the world, with herself, but most of all, with Rosco Hamden.

The words of a song came into her head. *I've had a love of my own* ... All those lovers lying in each other's arms—they need not look upon her with pity now. Nor need she look upon them with envy and a kind of anguish. There must after all be something about her, something she had long ago decided she did not possess, which made a man want to hold her like this, kiss her as Rosco had done, feel desire stirring for her. It would have been heaven, she thought with a thrust of sadness, if he had loved her, too ...

'Lisette?'

'Yes?' She rubbed her cheek against his.

'You'll come back to my flat?'

The long silence was broken by the agitated movements of her limbs. He must have felt them because his arms about her tightened. Did they give away the tumult in her mind, the battle she was fighting?

She prevaricated, putting off the moment of decision. 'You don't mean stay the night?'

He looked down at her with amusement. 'What else did you think I meant? To wash the dishes?'

She tried to smile. Her heart thudded painfully. His hand pushed between them intimately and pressed against her body where the heartbeats could be felt. 'Calm down, sweetheart. I'll be as tender and kind as you want me to be—the first time.'

'If—if it's what you want,' she whispered, 'I will.'

He said nothing, but she knew by the way his arms settled more firmly round her that she had pleased him. 'Later,' she said.

'Later,' he agreed.

Her thoughts wandered. She endeavoured to remember what he had told her about management. Even the small amount he had taught her indicated how very much there was to learn. Things would be so different from now on. Being part of a giant company would have its compensations, she supposed, however much she had condemned it in the past.

No more worries about finance—there would be more than sufficient money to develop and expand. Responsibilities would be shared, advisers on policy, on new markets and overseas trade would abound. Fear of strikes through failing to implement wage agreements would cease to exist.

'Oh, Rosco,' she stirred, 'it will be wonderful to be part of your company, to be the manager of a brand new factory, with modern machinery and proper office accommodation for the admin staff. You don't know how terrible it's been working in those old shacks and huts and in unhygienic conditions. When the new factory's equipped and we move in, I'll be able to——'

'*You'll* be able to?' She had not noticed until he spoke that his hold had loosened, that his arms were freeing her. 'To what?' Now she noticed the edge to his voice.

She felt cold, although the sun filtered warmly through the trees. She sat up, hugging her knees again.

'To be a better manager, I was going to say,' she said, frowning.

All around were blackberry bushes, at this time of the year full of thorns but no fruit. Long brambles stretched out as if trying to reach something that was just beyond them. The sun went behind a cloud and the treetops stirred in the sudden cool breeze.

Rosco sat up and the look he turned on her was cold. 'Let's get this straight. I have never once said, either by implication or firm statement, that you would be made manager of the new factory.'

'But, Rosco, I——' She was too dismayed to continue. The truth was taking time to penetrate.

'You—what?' He stood, pushing hands into pockets. 'Was that what this'—he indicated where they had been lying—'was all in aid of? Were you trying it on again? Was it a repeat performance of the last time you tried to persuade me, against my will, to take your company over?'

She stood now and faced him, her face pale, her hands clenched to stop the shaking.

'What was this—this human sacrifice in aid of this time?' he went on coldly. 'Last time it was for Big Business. For what reason did you see fit to use your "persuasive techniques" on this occasion? To make sure you got the managership of the new shoe company?'

Lisette shook her head, but it made no impression. How could she tell him she had seen no need to try 'persuasive techniques', as he called it? It would have sounded so arrogant, so presumptuous, to tell him she had assumed without question that the job would pass to her. After all, she had held the position before.

'So you were coming back to my flat? Why?' Rosco spoke harshly. 'For a repeat of what happened before, except that this time you were determined to go through with it right to the sigh of contentment at the end, followed by my unquestioning acquiescence to your request while still wrapped about by the golden aura of lovemaking?'

'Must you be so cynical?' she cried.

'Who was it this time who persuaded you to make the "sacrifice"?' he rasped. 'Your mother again, or your so understanding boy-friend, hoping he'd get a foot in the door, too, by becoming your assistant manager?'

She sat down again, drawing up her knees and resting her cheek on them. 'You're wrong in all your assumptions,' she choked. She knew she would be unable to convince him. Hadn't the events of the day followed, in his eyes, almost exactly what had taken place a week or two ago at his flat, when she had really tried to throw herself at him in order to gain his help?

'I'll take you home,' he said curtly.

So the golden day was over. That 'love of her own' had changed back into a remote stranger. 'All the way?' she asked dully, looking up at him.

He shrugged as if it was of no consequence how far he drove her as long as he deposited her somewhere away from him. He indicated that she should move from the old raincoat on which they had been lying. He folded it and pushed it into the holdall. The day which had held such promise had come to a bitter end.

They drove away from the peacefulness of Epping Forest into the endless movement of traffic that passed through the suburbs of London, the residential areas and industrial buildings which lined the route to her home.

'Did you honestly believe,' said Rosco, his voice hard, 'that, given the right kind of "encouragement", I would hand over on a plate the job of manager of the new shoe factory?'

'I've been its manager up to now,' she replied defensively, 'so I thought——'

'That you could make the transition from the management of a broken-down, failing firm to that of a brand new, properly financed venture without any trouble at all? And with what qualifications—that of once having been a *librarian*?'

'That was what Bob Farrell was—a librarian. Yet you've spoken well of him, called him able and intelligent——'

'Which he is.'

'Because he's a man, that's why! You're prejudiced against women in management positions, in any responsible position. You could never look on a woman as your equal——'

'I called you my equal once,' he broke in coldly.

'In fun, that's all. You didn't really mean it,' she accused. 'We were both managing directors, you said. The fact is,' she rounded on him, 'that you regard all women as suitable for only one thing, the appeasement of your desires.'

'You're talking the most unmitigated rubbish!'

'According to you, that's all I do talk.'

He laughed. 'Now you're wanting me to say that you're the most intelligent girl I know. All right,' with a quick glance at her, 'I will say it. You're the most intelligent girl I——'

'Then why can't you give me the managership of the new factory?'

'Never miss a chance, do you?' he taunted.

Most of the traffic lights seemed to be against them. During the long wait at each red signal, Lisette fretted. 'I hope,' she began as they waited for traffic to cross their path, 'you won't hold—what happened today against Bob Farrell.' Rosco was silent, his hands resting lightly on the steering wheel. 'He had no connection with—with today at all. Nor did my mother.'

'There's no need to try to protect your boy-friend,' he replied curtly. 'Where someone's business potential is concerned, I consider it not in relation to their private lives but their abilities.' The traffic lights changed and they moved on. 'So the motivation for the pathetic attempt at self-sacrifice today and your agreement to come back with me to my flat were motivated purely by self-interest?'

'I suppose,' she replied tiredly, 'you could think of it that way.'

By the tightening of his lips she knew what he was thinking. But wasn't it true? What else had brought her out to picnic with him—to tell him her feelings about him and to allow him to make love to her—if it hadn't been self-interest? Not, as he mistakenly believed, as a means of being given the managership of the new factory—she had assumed the job was hers anyway—but as a means of spending a few precious hours with him. 'Pathetic self-sacrifice' he had called it, when all she had wanted to do was to tell him, and show him, how much she loved him.

It seemed a long journey to her home. When Rosco drew up outside the house, she asked him in, but he refused. 'I'll call and see the Burlingtons. Thank you all the same. Goodbye, Lisette.'

She looked at him. 'Goodbye', he had said, and with such cool detachment. The word sounded so final. Was it really the end of everything between them?

CHAPTER EIGHT

A few days later, Lisette took a call from Rosco's secretary.

'Mr Hamden would like to see you, Miss Baird. Could you make it this afternoon?'

'See me?' Lisette asked, dazed and sounding, she knew, a little stupid. 'But why?'

'I really don't know, Miss Baird.'

Of course she wouldn't know, Lisette reproached herself. He wouldn't tell his secretary his private business, would he?

'What time this afternoon?' she asked.

'Three o'clock. On the dot, he says,' the girl said, laughing.

On the dot he was, too. At three o'clock precisely, Lisette was called from the waiting room and shown into Rosco's room. As she entered, he rose from the depths of one of the armchairs.

He approached, hand outstretched. 'Welcome once again to the executive suite.'

Lisette put her hand in his to acknowledge the polite gesture—and found hers caught and held fast. Her eyes were ensnared, too, and a slow smile spread across his face. 'Do you still like my touch?' He was being sarcastic again. 'Out of all the men in this world, do you still prefer mine?'

So he hadn't really believed what she had told him the other day in the forest? But how could he, when he had afterwards accused her of using her femininity as a bait to capture a top job?

'When we parted you said goodbye,' she answered. 'I thought you meant it.'

'In the personal sense I did.' His eyes did not leave her face which, to her own surprise, she managed to keep completely blank. 'In the business sense, I should have said au revoir. After all, we did buy you up. In the circumstances, you could hardly have expected not to see me again, could you?'

She took her hand from his. 'The day we first met,' she said, 'you gave due warning—that you "ate little companies like mine for your mid-morning snack".

He smiled. 'I seem to remember that when the "meal" was first offered to me, I turned my head away in disgust. Some time later, I recall a certain—attractive representative from that company virtually begging me to swallow it whole. I don't usually touch "failing" companies. But for some reason that completely escapes me,' he rubbed his jaw, 'I made an exception of that particular firm and complied.'

'We'll do our best not to give you "indigestion",' she retorted.

Rosco laughed.

'But,' she went on, 'as I'm to be thrown out of my job, I soon won't have any control over what happens to the firm called Baird Shoes. Or any connection with the company that made a meal of it.'

His eyes narrowed momentarily, then he motioned her towards the settee. 'Relax in the arms of your "parent" company.' His eyes mocked her, trailing her face and figure reminiscently, as though his thoughts were pleasant.

She coloured slightly and sank on to the settee. He joined her, leaning back and looking her over. The navy blue dress she wore was neat, button-through and round-necked. Her gloves, handbag and shoes were white. She was dressed as if she were attending an interview.

Rosco's hand moved towards her and rested a finger's touch from her thigh. She tingled, as if he were actually touching her. He smiled, as if he knew the effect the nearness of his hand was having on her.

'Well?' he murmured. 'Are the barriers up or down?'

'I don't know what you mean,' she answered stiffly.

'If the barriers are down, my sweet, you're welcome at my flat at any time.'

Her head spun round. 'Your woman friend called Wanda has left you, so you're looking for a replacement? Is that why you asked me here?'

He laughed, as if he was enjoying himself. 'You're wrong. Wanda has not "left" me. She comes and goes as she pleases. But no, that isn't why I asked you to come and see me.' He stood up, placing himself in front of her, growing brisk and serious. 'I called you here to offer you a job.'

'There's no need.'

'Why, have you found employment?' She shook her head. 'Then there's every need. You used to be a librarian. Is that right?'

'Yes,' she said, holding her breath.

'This company, like most large companies, possesses a library—a very good one. We need a librarian. I'm offering you the post.'

Her heart almost stopped. It was a dream—it must be!

'The library,' he went on, 'occupies all of the fifth floor of this administrative building. The pay is good, the hours are reasonable. It's a specialised field, but I'm sure that with your intelligence you would master it quickly. Will you accept?'

Her eyes came alive, her wide mouth curved in a smile. 'Rosco, I—I hardly know how to thank you. It's unbelievable! To be among books again ...'

He smiled at her pleasure.

'Are there many other librarians employed there?' she asked.

'I forget the exact number. There's the chief librarian—that would be you——'

'Me?'

'Yes, you. Why are you so surprised? Do you think,' with a smile, 'I would offer the one-time owner-manager of a shoe factory a lesser position, especially as she's had previous and very valuable experience in a library?'

'But——' Couldn't he hear the note of dismay in her voice?

'But what?' He seemed puzzled.

'You did say the position was that of *head* librarian?'

'I did. We shall, of course, require a reference from your former employers, but from all that I know of the applicant,' he smiled again, 'I have no doubt that it will be a good one.'

'Qualifications?'

'At least an A.L.A., Associate of the Library Association. Better still, the higher qualification of Fellow of that same association.'

She stood rigidly, doing her best to disguise her disappointment. 'Then I'm wasting your time.'

He frowned, caught her shoulders and urged her down again. 'Explain.'

Lisette said tonelessly, 'I have no qualifications as a librarian. I've taken no examinations. I haven't even attended library school.' Confessing the truth about herself to this highly-qualified man was acutely painful. 'The local branch library,' she went on, 'accepted me on the staff as a school-leaver and I remained an assistant all the time I was there.'

His frown deepened and he walked about, fingers scooping at the loose change in his pockets. 'Well,' he looked down at her, in his face dismissal, in his tone a touch of exasperation as if he had done his best for her and she had let him down, 'that's that, isn't it?'

'Rosco,' she looked up at him, 'you once called me so intelligent I understood everything you said without having to explain it in words of one syllable. Wouldn't that do, Rosco?' She was pleading, but was that so wrong when her livelihood was at stake?

He walked away, walked back. 'I haven't forgotten. It was at my flat. The circumstances were bordering on the—intimate. What I say when I have a——' his eyes skimmed over her, 'a playful kitten to entertain cannot be taken out of context and put into a business situation.' He walked away again and stood at the window gazing down at the insect-small traffic below.

'Thanks,' she hit back bitterly, 'I appreciate that, *very* much. I'll know in future never to accept what you say as the truth.'

He swung round, started to speak but changed his mind, turning back to the window.

'The job of manager of the new factory should be mine,' she burst out. Why should she not speak her mind? Where Electro-Magnetic Universal was concerned, she had nothing to lose any more. Her eyes, full of challenge, sought his. He looked at her. She wished he would speak.

At last he said, 'There's no reason at all why you shouldn't send in your application along with other people when the job's advertised. But I warn you, you may not even be short-listed. We shall want a person of the highest calibre, wide experience and preferably a degree in management. Do you honestly consider that you'd qualify, even for an interview?'

'It's ironic,' she said bitterly, acknowledging in her heart that he was right, 'that the lower down the industrial ladder you are, the more you're taken care of. My employees are assured of their jobs, but I——'

'I said you could apply although, as I also said, you'll be up against stiff opposition. *If* you succeeded, you would also be entering the rat race, Lisette. Are you up to that?'

'What do you mean?' she challenged. 'Am I healthy enough? Authoritative enough? Can I get nasty enough when the necessity arises? Or is it again because I'm the "wrong" sex—I'm female and therefore in your eyes weaker than my male counterpart?'

His hand came out and he lifted her by the elbow to stand in front of him. He looked at the high colour in her cheeks, the blaze in her eyes. 'Nothing will quell that spirit of yours, will it?'

She gazed back at him unflinchingly, unwilling to drop the subject because it was her future she was fighting for. But she would not get down on her knees and beg for the job.

His arms encircled her waist and he impelled her towards him. The sweet familiarity of the feel of his body against hers and the male scent of him drove every rational thought from her head.

'Must we keep fighting?' he murmured, resting his lips first against her ear, then trailing her cheek to her mouth, where his lingered.

Lisette fought to quieten her hammering heart, to regain control of her powers of reason. He lifted her chin. 'Be truthful with yourself, Lisette. Do you really think you could tackle such a position?'

With a jerk she was almost free of him. This was a man to be fought, not tamely submitted to. 'That's typical of you,' she accused. 'First you kiss me, then you stick a knife in my back!'

The phone rang and he released her to answer it. 'John Waterman? Yes, I want to speak to him. Put him through in two minutes.' He covered the mouthpiece and turned to her, but she was already at the door.

'If you have any more bright ideas for jobs for me,' she snapped, 'go a little lower down the social scale. I might *just* have enough intelligence to become a

175

cleaner, or if I'm not up to that, I could always make the tea.'

He was angry and did not hide it.

'All right,' she flung across the room, 'so I'm being unjust. You've done your best for me. But,' she blazed, 'I'm a failure—at *everything*. Can't you get that into your head? And I'll tell you something else. I don't care, I just don't care any more!'

She slammed the door and ran along the corridor knowing that she did care. She cared very much indeed.

Two weeks later, Bob Farrell received a call from the head of Electro-Magnetic Universal.

'Mr Hamden wants to see me,' he said. 'I don't know why. Any ideas, Lisette?'

She shook her head. How was she to know how Rosco Hamden's mind worked—except against *her* interests?

Bob kissed her lightly on the cheek as he left to catch the train to London. 'For luck,' he laughed. He needn't have said that, Lisette thought as he went to the door. She knew it was not for love of her!

'I'll ring you at home,' he said, 'and let you know what it was all about.'

The takeover of Baird Shoes by Electro-Magnetic had gone smoothly. Now cash-flow was assured and finance was no longer a problem, the employees' wages had been increased. Their future had no question mark hanging over it. Lisette thought it was ironic that the only one who did not know where she was going was the one-time owner of the firm. Bob could, if he liked, either find another job in industry or return to librarianship.

He phoned her that evening. He sounded so excited she knew something good had happened to him.

'Mr Hamden offered me a job, Lisette,' Bob said. 'As assistant manager.'

'Assistant manager of what?' she asked dazedly.

'You know, in the new shoe company. They're going to change its name, of course,' Bob went on before she could say a word. 'Can't be Baird Shoes any more, can it? I suggested "Soft Stepper Shoes". Mr Hamden thought the name might be taken up by them.'

Choking back her feelings, Lisette managed to congratulate him. 'When do you start?' she asked.

'As soon as it can be arranged. There'll be a smooth switch from my present position to the new one. He's told me to work on some draft plans for the re-organisation. I told him I'd already had some ideas and he wants to see them.'

'Who's the manager you'll be assisting, Bob?' She tried to make her voice sound disinterested.

'They're going to advertise. He said it would have been stupid to advertise for an assistant manager when he knew I'd make such a good one!'

Lisette remembered how Rosco had referred with respect to Bob Farrell's intelligence. But, she thought in anguish, he had said he respected hers, too!

Bob was saying, 'It will mean my moving house. I'll have to find new lodgings. You don't object if I move away, do you, Lisette?' He asked the question a little uncertainly. What did he expect her to do—grow hysterical?

'Of course not, Bob. The sky's the limit for you, now. With Electro-Magnetic behind you, you'll get to the top one day.'

And it was I, Lisette thought ironically, who was at that "top" once! And it was I to whom Rosco gave instruction in the art of management, not Bob.

'Good,' said Bob. 'I knew you'd see it that way.' He rang off.

What he had really meant, Lisette thought, turning away, was, I'm glad we haven't got our lives so entangled with each other's that you thought I was going

177

to marry you. I'm glad you haven't made a fuss and that I'm still free of all ties.

Lisette's mother was spending the evening with the Burlingtons. When the phone rang, Lisette thought it was her mother. It was Rosco.

'Well,' he said, 'heard the great news yet?'

'What news?' Although her heart was thudding, her voice was dead.

'I thought you'd be out—or in—with your boy-friend. Celebrating his new job.'

'That's his affair, not mine.'

A brittle pause. 'I thought,' the speaker continued, 'he would have come round to your house tonight and proposed marriage. After all, today he got himself a brand new job, at a much higher salary, with excellent prospects. What better basis for a good marriage partnership could a couple want than that?'

Lisette imagined the sarcastic smile on the face of the caller. Would it deepen to cynicism after she had spoken?

'I may be old-fashioned,' she said slowly, 'but there is that little thing called love.'

She would never know the response she had provoked in him because he rang off. The noise the receiver made crashing on to its cradle was painful to her ear. She rubbed it and sighed.

What had she said to make him angry? Or had Wanda arrived unexpectedly? 'She comes and goes as she pleases,' he'd said. Had he perhaps become impatient with the boring girl called Lisette Baird to whom he had been speaking?

Her hair needed washing. She looked in the hall mirror and made a face at herself. No wonder Rosco had cut their conversation short! If the face that stared back at her was compared with that of the woman called Wanda, the face in the mirror would lose out every time.

Lisette pulled off her dress and put on a towelling robe. She shampooed her hair and rinsed it with the shower attachment over the bath. There was a noise behind her and she listened, decided she must have imagined it, turned off the water and groped for the towel.

It was put into her hand. She gripped it and with her hair dripping freely over the bath said tensely, 'Mother?'

There was no reply. Frightened, she straightened and swung round, spraying herself and the floor around her with water from her soaking hair.

'Rosco!' It was a shriek.

He stood in the doorway, resting on his hand against the frame. The familiar taunting smile curved his lips. His wine-red shirt was open at the neck. His dark-brown trousers fitted him to perfection.

Lisette's heart did its usual dance at the sight of him. She said sharply, to hide her confusion, 'It's not long since you phoned. How did you get here so fast?'

'I stole a jet and flew here. It's parked in the back garden.'

She frowned at his broad smile. 'Don't be silly. Anyway, how did you get in?'

He held up a bunch of keys.

'My mother's?' He nodded. 'But she's at the Burlingtons'.'

'So was I. You'd been invited, too. Why didn't you come?'

'I didn't feel sociable. Anyway, it's none of your business.' She turned her back on him, hoping he would take the hint. 'I still don't feel sociable.'

'That's okay by me. Carry on. Pretend I'm not here.'

That was asking the impossible! She lifted the towel to dry her hair and turned to face him.

'Don't you know,' she said desperately, 'that a woman never likes to be seen washing her hair?'

'Not being a woman,' he returned dryly, 'I wouldn't.'

'Hasn't Wanda ever told you?' She hoped he would recognise the sarcasm, but it seemed he didn't.

He pushed his fingers back through his hair. 'Wanda?' he murmured, affecting a frown. 'Who's Wanda?'

'Oh!' She turned from him. 'Will you please go away?'

In the silence she rubbed the towel slowly over her wet hair.

'Now that's no way to treat a visitor.' He must have crept across the room because, when his hands settled on her shoulders, she reacted violently. One twist and she was free, facing him, breathing hard.

'Why have you come?' she demanded. 'To offer me another job? As a lift attendant, perhaps? Or haven't I got enough *experience* for that? Licking envelopes? No,' she shook her head furiously, spattering him with water, but he merely smiled, 'I've no qualifications for that, so that's no good. Emptying ashtrays? Worse still. We don't smoke here, so how could I have ever emptied ashtrays before?'

Rosco stood, arms across his chest, hands gripping each elbow. There was amusement in his eyes and also a tantalisingly veiled look. He seemed to be enjoying a private joke which excluded her, and it riled her beyond all reason.

'I came to ask you a question,' he said at last.

'You could have asked that on the phone,' she snapped, rubbing so hard at her hair it was beginning to resemble a bush.

He shook his head. 'Not this question. I wanted to see your face when you answered.'

She covered her face with the damp towel. 'Now ask it.'

He threw back his head and laughed. After a moment he said abruptly, 'Remove that towel, Lisette.'

There was a note in his voice that demanded to be obeyed. The towel was lifted to her head again.

'Are you in love?'

The towel stayed still, dismay filled her eyes. Had he guessed her secret? 'Who with?' she parried.

'Bob Farrell?'

'Good heavens, no!' She gasped and the towel covered her mouth. Now what would he think? He was quick-witted, he knew she had no other boy-friend.

'So you won't be going with him when he moves? You won't be finding a house to live in, marry him and live happily ever after?'

'I've told you—no, *no*!' She added, with an acrimony which took even herself by surprise, 'Anyway, how many marriages these days have a "storybook" ending? Tell me anything, *anything* in life,' her voice rose, 'that ends happily?'

He walked across to her, but she swung from him. Again his hands found her shoulders, but this time they slipped under the bath robe and moved and moulded caressingly. 'How bitter my little worker-director has grown since I've known her. Can she tell me why?'

'Why?' she blazed, wrenching away again and facing him. 'Wouldn't you have become bitter if, like me, you'd had everything taken from you?'

'By "everything",' he said quietly, pocketing his hands, 'do you mean Bob Farrell? He's getting promotion, has excellent prospects and you don't want to stand in his way? So you're doing the great self-sacrificial act I know so well and denying you love him?'

Lisette pulled the robe back over her shoulders and wrapped it defensively about her. She asked, her voice brittle, 'Is it your guilty conscience that makes you keep going back monotonously to my friendship, and I mean friendship, with Bob?'

He looked astonished and quite unamused. 'Why

should *I* have a guilty conscience where you're concerned?'

'You?' she spat, uncaring of any injustice of which she might be accused. 'You took away from me everything that made life worth living—the factory, my work, my interests, the ideas I was going to try out where Baird Shoes were concerned.'

'Such as?' he asked coldly.

She sank on to the side of the bath. 'Oh—oh, I don't know.' Why was she so confused? She gave a quick rub over her hair, then stopped. 'Like—like a workers' co-operative. That's the future,' she flared, her eyes burning, 'whether you, from your pinnacle of industrial power, like it or not.'

Rosco was silent, considering her drooping figure.

'All I wanted,' she said forlornly, 'was a loan, some money so that I could try to put my ideas into practice.' She glanced up at him. 'And you wouldn't give it to me.'

'You must face facts, Lisette.' She seemed to have stirred him to anger, but, she told herself, she should be used to that by now, shouldn't she? 'A mere loan would have been useless. Such a venture wouldn't have succeeded without a massive injection of new capital, and you damned well know it! Your credit-worthiness was so poor no bank or financial concern would have advanced you a single penny.'

She closed her eyes. They were quarrelling again. When would he go? His presence in such intimate circumstances was torturing her. But it seemed he had not yet had his say.

'Have you thought,' he said quietly, 'just what I have given you? A large amount of money—much larger than my auditors told me your firm was worth—to buy you out. Out of your difficulties, your money troubles, your strike threats, your ancient method of production, your failure to provide the goods on time. Not to mention the means to repay your overdraft which the bank manager was demanding back. Is that *nothing*?'

'I'm sorry,' she said wearily. 'It's all true. You've won. But then,' her hair hung down wetly and she pushed it aside, 'you always win.'

'I wouldn't be where I was now if I didn't.'

She stared at the bath mat beneath her bare feet and considered his remark. She considered it all ways. It could—just possibly—hold a double meaning.

Her head lifted. 'What do you mean?'

He came to sit beside her on the edge of the bath. His arm went round her shoulders. 'Let me see,' he smiled down at her, 'it all began two or three months ago, when I saw a girl across a crowded room.'

Lisette's heart began to hammer, but her eyes were wary. Failure and disappointment had stared her in the face so many times in her life she could not believe she was free of their tormenting presence now.

With a shy, tentative smile, she looked at him.

'I'm offering that girl a job.'

Her smile vanished. 'Not again!' she said angrily.

'Yes, again.' He caught her chin and, overcoming her resistance, turned her face to his. 'The job I'm offering is full-time, well-paid, has limitless possibilities.' A short silence, then, 'Although you haven't asked, I'll tell you what that job entails. It involves cooking for me, entertaining for me——'

'As your *housekeeper*?'

He laughed loudly and continued, 'To live with me, sleep with me, and most important of all, make love with me.'

'As your *woman*?'

'As my woman.'

'You mean take the place of Wanda?'

It seemed she had annoyed him again. 'I wouldn't speak of you both in the same breath.'

So he rated Wanda's attractions more highly than

hers! 'No, thank you,' she retorted. 'I haven't enough *experience*. I haven't any qualifications.' She held out her ringless hands. 'I haven't any previous knowledge——'

'By heaven, the woman has wit, not to mention a biting tongue. It must be the wet hair that's doing it. Here, let me dry it.' He seized the towel, stood up and rubbed her hair until she shrieked.

'Stop it! Stop it, please!'

'If I do, will you behave?'

'Yes, oh, yes!'

He looked around. 'This is ridiculous. I've never found such an uncomfortable place to sit in my life, especially with a girl. On the side of a bath, indeed!' He scooped her into his arms and looked down into her face. 'Where's your room?'

'Put me down at once,' she demanded, kicking her legs, but he held her easily. 'Anyway, we can't go in my room. I'm not dressed——'

'Precisely,' he said dryly. 'It's the best place to be when you're, as they say, *déshabillée*. And I might remind you that you've been in *my* bedroom.' He smiled into her eyes. 'Haven't you? Yes, you might blush, young woman. An innocent like you trying to seduce a man like me! Now,' on the landing, 'which one?' He followed her pointing finger. 'A single bed? M'm, I disapprove of that. However, it will do for now.'

She cried in alarm, 'What do you mean, for now? What are you intending——?'

'I'll come to that later,' he said enigmatically, putting her down and sitting beside her. 'Listen to me first.' He folded his arms and looked her over, seeing her fluffy hair, her pink cheeks, her eyes so bright it was as though there was a light glowing behind them.

'As I mentioned just now,' he said, 'it all began when I saw you across that crowded room at the Chamber of Trade reception.'

'When I choked after drinking that brandy?'

'That moment exactly. I said to myself, "That's the one. She'll be mine even if I have to move mountains to get her."'

'But'—Lisette frowned—'I thought you were laughing at me.'

'I was. As people laugh when they find treasure at the end of a lifetime's search. Yes, my bright-eyed spitfire, I mean what I'm saying. I've been intoxicated with you from the moment our eyes first met. You got into my bloodstream and you've been going round me ever since. Why do you think I persuaded my Board of Directors to buy Baird Shoes if not because I'd fallen in love with you? The money you were given was really a gift, because financially your company had little value. Why do you think I kept trying to fit you into a job with Emu if not to please you and help you?'

He drew her against him, holding her throat and tilting her head. 'Don't you think, my sweet, it's time you thanked me properly for all I've done for you?'

'How, Rosco?' she whispered.

His mouth approached her lips. 'This,' he murmured against them, 'will do very nicely for the moment.'

When at last the kissing had ended, leaving Lisette resting limply against him, she sighed and said, 'I fell in love with you at the reception, too. Which means that I loved you that day I came to your flat. I would never have——'

'Offered yourself?' he put in teasingly.

She nodded.

'Why didn't you tell me, wench?' he asked softly, pushing aside her bathrobe and feathering her shoulders with his lips.

'That I——' She took a breath to steady herself, because his kisses were undermining her self-control. 'That I loved you? You wouldn't have believed me, would you? You'd have thought I had only said it for my own ends.'

'Would I? Who knows? Who cares?' He whispered, 'Put your arms around me, darling.'

She complied, unbuttoning his shirt with a shy kind of boldness and slipping her arms beneath it. Then her cheek found his hard chest.

'Docile suddenly, aren't you?' he teased softly.

Indignantly she started to draw away, but he pulled her back, laughing. 'Good! I love that spirit of yours. It challenges me, it provokes me. Keep it up throughout our married life and I'll——'

Her head jerked back and she shot at him, 'Who said we're marrying?'

'I did. Your mother knows, because I told her before I left her. The Burlingtons know, because they were there, too.'

'But you haven't asked me yet!'

'I have no intention,' he said, smiling arrogantly. 'I'm telling you.' He grasped a handful of her hair and pulled back her head. 'So you don't like monopolies, my little spitfire? And you don't like takeovers? Too bad, my darling, because from now on I'm acting the big bad boss. I'm monopolising you. I'm taking you over from here,' he tugged her hair and she squealed, 'to here.' He dived and grasped her ankle. 'Do you understand? Unless,' with a wicked twinkle, 'you'd rather live with me without any ceremony, legal ties, ring, certificate—need I go on?'

'I'll marry you,' she whispered joyfully. 'Any time, any place. Now, if you like. Oh, Rosco,' she reached up and pressed her lips to his, 'I love you so much . . .'

The robe, which he had loosened, fell from her shoulders. The frail barriers which were left between them were no obstacles to his caresses.

Later, he said as she gazed dreamily into his eyes, 'You know how the song goes? *Once you have found her, never let her go.* From the moment I met you one enchanted evening, that piece of advice has influenced my every action where you're concerned. And I promise you, my love, that it will go on doing so for the rest of our lives.'

She sighed and settled even more closely into his arms.

Harlequin Plus

A WORD ABOUT THE AUTHOR

Lilian Peake grew up in North Essex, a region about sixty miles northeast of London, England. She became secretary to a local mystery author, gaining valuable insight into how an author functions.

Before she wrote her first Harlequin, Lilian also worked as a journalist, a career that included a stint with a London fashion magazine. This experience was to help with background for her fourth novel, *The Real Thing* (Harlequin Romance #1650). Unlike her mystery-author employer, who dictated his work, Lilian found she had to type her manuscripts herself. "I have to see my thoughts in front of my eyes," she explains.

Though two of her book titles are *Master of the House* and *Man in Charge*, Lilian maintains that women should play a much bigger role in running the world than they do at present. To this end, she believes, education is the key.

Lilian Peake's first Harlequin, *This Moment in Time* (Romance #1572), was published in 1972.

What readers say about Harlequin Romances

"I feel as if I am in a different world every time I read a Harlequin."
A.T.,* Detroit, Michigan

"Harlequins have been my passport to the world. I have been many places without ever leaving my doorstep."
P.Z., Belvedere, Illinois

"I like Harlequin books because they tell so much about other countries."
N.G., Rouyn, Quebec

"Your books offer a world of knowledge about places and people."
L.J., New Orleans, Louisiana

"Your books turn my...life into something quite exciting."
B.M., Baldwin Park, California

"Harlequins take away the world's troubles
and for a while you can live in a world of
your own where love reigns supreme."
   L.S.,* Beltsville, Maryland

"Thank you for bringing romance back
to me."
   J.W., Tehachapi, California

"I find Harlequins are the only stories on
the market that give me a satisfying
romance with sufficient depth without
being maudlin."
   C.S., Bangor, Maine

"Harlequins are magic carpets...away from
pain and depression...away to other people
and other countries one might never know
otherwise."
   H.R., Akron, Ohio

*Names available on request

SUPERROMANCE

Longer, exciting, sensual and dramatic!

Fascinating love stories that will hold
you in their magical spell till the last page
is turned!

Now's your chance to discover the earlier
books in this exciting series. Choose from
the great selection on the following page!

Choose from this list of great

SUPERROMANCES!

SUPERROMANCE

Complete and mail this coupon today!

- -

Worldwide Reader Service

In the U.S.A.
1440 South Priest Drive
Tempe, AZ 85281

In Canada
649 Ontario Street
Stratford, Ontario N5A 6W2

Please send me the following SUPERROMANCES. I am enclosing my check or money order for $2.50 for each copy ordered, plus 75¢ to cover postage and handling.

☐ #1 END OF INNOCENCE   ☐ #6 SWEET SEDUCTION
☐ #2 LOVE'S EMERALD FLAME   ☐ #7 THE HEART REMEMBERS
☐ #3 THE MUSIC OF PASSION   ☐ #8 BELOVED INTRUDER
☐ #4 LOVE BEYOND DESIRE   ☐ #9 SWEET DAWN OF DESIRE
☐ #5 CLOUD OVER PARADISE   ☐ #10 HEART'S FURY

Number of copies checked @ $2.50 each =	$_____
N.Y. and Ariz. residents add appropriate sales tax	$_____
Postage and handling	$_____.75
TOTAL	$_____

I enclose_____.
(Please send check or money order. We cannot be responsible for cash sent through the mail.)
Prices subject to change without notice.

NAME_____
                    (Please Print)
ADDRESS_____
CITY_____
STATE/PROV._____
ZIP/POSTAL CODE_____

Offer expires June 30, 1982   110562623